Brethren Trail Blazers

BRETHREN TRAIL BLAZERS

Mary Garber and Others

Illustrated by Harry Durkee

THE BRETHREN PRESS
ELGIN, ILLINOIS

Printed in the United States of America

Contents

Thinking About Trail Blazers

Pam looked up from her Bible, her eyes shining with the pleasure of discovery. "To be a Christian is to have adventures!" she exclaimed.

The teacher and the other girls and boys in Pam's church-school class were thoughtful. They remembered stories of followers of Jesus, stories in the Bible and in other books. Truly, these Christians had adventures. Many of them found new ways to show what it means to be a Christian.

The Christians whose stories we can read in this book lived bravely. They had adventures. They were trail blazers. As we read their stories we can go adventuring with them along the trails they blazed.

Each of us can be a trail blazer. "How can I be a trail blazer?" someone asks. "There are no unexplored continents. Any place I can think of has already been discovered." But a trail blazer does not have to go somewhere. He can think new thoughts about what it means to be a Christian in this new age. Who knows what adventures are ahead for Christians in this universe that is bigger than the greatest scientists can measure?

Perhaps not many of us will have our life stories written in books, but we can have adventures. We can be trail blazers. We can be Christians!

— Hazel M. Kennedy
Church of the Brethren General Offices
Elgin, Illinois

The Founder of Our Church

ALEXANDER MACK, SR. (1679-1735)

"Anybody might have done it,
But His whisper came to me."

In slightly different words, Rudyard Kipling said it. But Alexander Mack lived it. And God can use a humble person who earnestly seeks the truth and who has the courage to follow His leading. This is Alexander Mack, the founder of the Church of the Brethren.

The world of Alexander Mack's day was dark and troubled. There were terrible wars. The churches did not help people to live better, and often people did not know what to do.

"Follow me," Jesus had said. "I am the way, the truth, and the life."

Alexander Mack listened. And because this man, and others like him, have tried simply to follow Christ's way of life, as recorded in the Bible, the destinies of our world have been affected.

When the world about them was torn by wars and confusion, these early Brethren founded a simple faith and practice that has stood the test of over two hundred fifty years.

It was on the twenty-seventh day of July in 1679 when there was an unusual stir in one of the best homes in the quiet village of Schriesheim, Germany.

Two neighbors stood on the street talking.

"Have you heard the news?" asked one.

"No. What news?" asked the other eagerly.

"The Macks have a new baby."

"You don't say! That makes eight children, doesn't it? Is the newcomer a girl or a boy?"

"It's a boy. He is their fourth son. I hear they are going to baptize him with the name, Alexander, after his uncle."

"Well, I'd say his father, John Philip Mack, will have need to do well with the mill he just bought, to feed that many children."

"Ah, yes" was the answer. "But I am sure he will. He is honest and he works hard. I heard it was over one hundred years ago that the first Mack bought a mill. I am very glad John got the chance to buy a mill in our village."

At first, little Alexander thought of the mill as an interesting place to go to and not as a place in which to earn a living. The mill stood on the banks of the Schriesheim Creek, and you may be sure the youngest son went to it as often as he could. His father and his two older brothers worked there. What little boy would miss such a chance as that? And there was the great water wheel that ran the mill! For hours, the small boy would watch the water tumbling over the wheel.

At times Alexander would run through the beautiful meadows. When he rested under a tree, he listened to the birds sing. Then his heart would sing, "God's world is beautiful." And when the wintertime laid a white blanket of snow over the village, his heart sang again, "God's world is beautiful and good." But always came this question: "Why cannot everyone be good and happy in such a beautiful world?"

It was when Alexander was ten years old that these happy, carefree days ended. His oldest brother, who was only twenty-four years old, died. This was a terrible experience for the boy. But the blow that followed was, perhaps, even worse.

Soon after this, Father Mack called all of the family together. Alexander looked at each face. He saw the sadness on the kind faces of his parents.

His father spoke slowly. "Jacob will now need some help in the mill since your oldest brother is gone. I cannot help much because of the gout in my foot and my job as councilman. Alexander will have to help."

In the silence that followed, the boy wondered if the others could hear his heart beating loudly.

"But, Father, my school . . . ?" His voice sounded strange and far away, even to him. But he couldn't help asking the question.

"My son, I know how much you had counted on going to college at Heidelberg," answered his father sadly. "After you had done so well in your studies in our village schools I had set my heart on it also. I spoke to your uncle, who is in charge of the school. But now, you must put this thought from your mind and learn the milling trade."

"It will serve the dreamer right," said Alexander's third brother in a hard, unkind voice. "It is time he learned to do something useful. He's no better than the rest of us. I had to learn the trade of a baker when there was no room for me in the mill."

So the career of Alexander Mack was decided. And one long, hard day followed another. There was little relief, except on Sunday. But he did not even look forward to Sunday.

Every Sunday found the Mack family in church. Father Mack was an elder in the Reformed church. He believed it was right to attend church. But many people

11

went only because they were afraid not to go. Church attendance was not the happy experience we know today. "I am very tired," thought the children. But they did not dare say so. Often the preacher raved against other churches, or preached about something that did not interest young people in the least. But the people had to go to church just the same. Life did not seem to hold much for Alexander.

But God's Spirit kept whispering to him. He thought about God. He asked himself many questions. He saw people in the church on Sunday and he saw those same people come to the mill on Monday to lie and cheat in their business dealings. Why did going to church every Sunday not make the people happier or better? Rough voices and unkind words were out of place in God's beautiful world.

Soon people began to notice the young miller. He grew tall and manly. He would have been noticed in any crowd. The mill paid well. People liked to do business with him.

More than one would say, "I'll wait for Alexander." Perhaps he would then explain to his neighbor, "He is always very friendly and he gives one his money's worth. One time, I saw him give double measure to a poor family. I trust a man like that."

Many people came to the mill to buy and sell. Alexander went to other villages to sell his flour and feed. Always, it made him sad to see church members, and even the preachers, act as if they had never heard of Jesus when they were doing business. He grew more and more unhappy in the state church.

"The Mennonites are different," he thought. "They are kind and gentle, even in business. I must know the answer."

So, like George Fox and the Quakers of England, he "sought heavenly wisdom with the Bible in his hand."

His belief that the religion of Jesus is not a long list of *do's* and *dont's*, but that it is a way of life, grew stronger. He was convinced that followers of Christ must live each day by Jesus' teachings in the New Testament. "Christians must live like Jesus," he thought. "He went about doing good."

There was one in the village who never grew tired of listening to Alexander's beliefs and dreams. She was Anna Margaret Kling. They were married on January 18, 1701. And she was in the group of eight who were the first members of the Church of the Brethren.

The development in German church life known as Pietism greatly influenced Mack. This was known as the religion-in-life movement. Many earnest souls turned Pietist in those troubled times. They formed little groups to study the Bible.

"Religion should help in everyday living," they said. "And above all, there must be no force in church matters."

Alexander Mack invited one of the leaders of this movement to his village. Ernest Hochmann and his friend Christian Erb came and began to hold meetings in the Mack mill. They preached in the streets and gave pamphlets to the workers returning from the fields. For this they were treated like the worst lawbreakers. Hochmann was sentenced to hard labor on a diet of bread and water. The ruler made a harsh law that any person suspected of Pietism was to be arrested without trial and put to hard labor.

It was then that Alexander Mack had to decide whether to continue the new teaching or not.

"Be strong," said God's Spirit. "Be loyal to your faith." Then he sold his half of the mill to his older brother.

"Let us go to Schwarzenau in the County of Wittgenstein," he said to his wife. "I have heard that there we may find peace and freedom to worship God as we choose."

"I am willing," bravely declared the young mother of his two little sons.

At Schwarzenau, the Macks were very happy to find others who believed as they did. These people had come from many provinces in which the rulers were unfriendly. Each ruler could decide which of the three state churches — the Catholic, the Lutheran, or the Reformed — should be the church of his province. Then everyone had to follow whether he believed the way that church did or not. Some of these people at Schwarzenau had given up everything they had for the right to think for themselves.

Much time was spent in Bible study and prayer. They were seeking God's will for their lives. They studied the history of the early church.

"We need a church," said Alexander Mack, as he listened to God's voice, "a church that will practice the teachings and the example of Jesus as found in the New Testament."

Each step was taken to God in prayer. It was tested by the Bible.

"You must count the cost of this baptism," warned Alexander Mack when the time of organization came. He wrote a hymn which begins with these words: "Christ Jesus says, 'Count well the cost.'"

Early one morning in 1708, eight brave and joyous souls walked down to the Eder River and were baptized. They had called upon Alexander Mack to do the baptizing. "No," said he. "I first need to be baptized correctly before I can baptize you." So they had cast lots to see which of the brethren should baptize Mack. Then he baptized the others. The Church of the Brethren had begun.

These five men and three women began a joyous witness to their faith. And the new church grew, with Alexander Mack as the leader. He kept right on preaching and baptizing even though the authorities threatened him with prison.

After twelve years, Alexander Mack had to leave Schwarzenau. He, with his congregation, went to Holland and finally came to America, where Peter Becker had settled part of the Krefeld congregation.

"We have been praying for you to come," the earlier Brethren settlers at Germantown told him.

Alexander Mack worked hard for six years with the church in America. Then God whispered to him, "Well done."

"Anybody might have done it,
But His whisper came to me."

— *Mary Garber*

A Quiet Hero for Christ

JOHN LOBACH (1689-1750)

"I am glad to give myself up to death for the sake of Christ, who gladdens my heart whenever I remember that this death opens the door for me to eternal bliss, and at the same time closes it on all suffering forever."

With these words, John Lobach wrote what he thought was his last letter to his mother. He had been imprisoned. Sentence was about to be passed. His crime? He had joined the Church of the Brethren!

This was Germany in 1717. If a person would not agree with one of the three religious groups allowed by the state he was considered a criminal. John Lobach had been a devout member of the Reformed (Presbyterian) church at Solingen, but he was disturbed at the difference between what was preached and what was practiced. Therefore he broke away from it.

He and several friends began to meet in small Bible-study groups in order to know God's Word and His will for them better. The church leaders, who were government officials, burst in upon them and attacked them severely for this. They shouted: "What! What! What are you doing here? Do we not have churches and houses of God for this? We are the ones appointed by God to teach and preach. How dare you gather like this to teach one another?"

Lobach replied modestly but firmly, "You are resisting in us the order of God, for we have a command that we should exhort one another daily in season and out of season. Why don't you criticize those of your congregation who carouse in the taverns all day and night, instead of disturbing our little meetings?"

The state clergymen expelled Lobach and his friends from the church and warned the government about their activities.

The uproar in the community was tremendous. After all, the Lobach family was one well known in this steel-making area. John's father, Peter, was a metal worker who specialized in the production of knives. Wanting his son to have a chance for education, he sent John to the Latin school. Here he did so well that many told the father that he should be sent on to a higher school to prepare for the ministry. But the necessary funds were lacking. John had to leave school to learn his father's trade.

Four years later, tragedy struck. French troops invaded that part of Germany. Peter Lobach was helping some neighbors cut down trees to block the roads. Suddenly, a body of French cavalry surprised them. Lobach was dragged by a French rider to a far-off city. Here he fell ill and died.

After recovering from his grief, John continued his father's business under great difficulties. With the strict discipline of his father no longer present, John began to live a careless and reckless life. He caused his mother great concern when he stayed out late in bad company. He also spent more than he could afford for fine clothes. In his heart he knew that he was doing wrong; yet he enjoyed his new freedom.

A severe illness lasting some months brought with it a deep experience — a conversion. John sincerely repented of his wasted years and determined that he would live his life in a truly Christian manner when he recovered.

As he was unable to resume his trade, young Lobach spent his time teaching the children here and there. He was also active in holding meetings in which he showed great gifts in speaking and praying. It was these meetings which caused the state clergy to attack him.

A visitor did much to strengthen his new convictions. This was Ernest Hochmann — the same Pietist nobleman who had influenced Alexander Mack and other early Brethren. During his stay in Solingen, Hochmann's preaching was so powerful that an eyewitness described the effect as if he lifted his hearers off the ground.

After the baptism of Lobach and his friends, the state clergy complained to the government. They kept it up until the group was arrested and marched off to another city under heavy guard. By singing hymns the whole way, Lobach and the others showed their confidence that God would look after them. After arriving at their prison late one night, they were told by the judges the next day that they could be released. Released, that is, if they would just promise to join either the Reformed, Lutheran, or Roman Catholic Church. They said they were determined to remain true to their faith.

Catholic and Lutheran clergy tried to persuade them with clever arguments, but had no success. Then threats were used. They were forced to listen to the pitiful cries of prisoners being tortured. Thumb screws and the terrible Spanish boot — a metal case with spikes inside which was tightened around the legs — were used. They were marched to the door of the torture chamber where the executioner was waiting for them. But the Brethren were resolved to hold firm, and no harm was done them. It was during this time that Lobach wrote the letter mentioned above.

Finally sentence was passed. Lobach and six others were sentenced to life imprisonment at hard labor. The harsh term was to be spent at a fortress called Jülich not far from the Dutch border.

When they arrived at Jülich, they were thrown into the common cell with other prisoners. It was called the Bacon Pantry, a grim reference to the many rats which lived there. The rough prisoners delighted in tormenting the Brethren. They put lice in their clothing and demanded gifts. Their jailors were also cruel, and even took away their precious Bibles.

Before long they were placed in other dungeons. At times they were two by two, and at times all together. Life was better when they were together because then they could help each other. Their underground cells had walls ten feet thick. Light came in only a few weeks each year when the sun shone at just the right angle through the thick bars. In the summertime they had to work twelve hours a day, but in the winter the shorter days meant that they had more time in their cells. Then they could make buttons by candlelight. They sold these and earned money to buy more food. Their jailors gave them only bread and water every few days.

They were not forgotten by their friends and brethren, however. The local people marveled at how many visitors came. Besides Brethren such as Alexander Mack and John Naas, Mennonites came from nearby Krefeld. Sometimes the visitors could arrange for better treatment for their friends.

The six men were soon so trusted that they were allowed to work outside the walls without a guard. This was true as long as one of them was still inside the prison. Their captors knew that none of the Brethren would ever run away from his friends.

Despite their cheerfulness and good humor, their life was miserable. Poor food, hard labor, and constant change between their ice-cold cells and hot outside work made them all sick. Lobach's mother received permission to come to the prison to care for her son. While there she caught the fever he had had, and died.

Just when their plight looked the darkest, help came. Some influential Dutchmen heard of their imprisonment. They took it up with their government. It happened at that time that the German ruler of the territory where the Solingen Brethren were imprisoned was eager to obtain something from the Dutch government. The Dutch told him that they would not agree as long as the Brethren were kept in prison. Thus it was that after four years the Solingen Brethren were released.

Great was the joy of John Naas and others in Krefeld when the six prisoners arrived. Weak and haggard from their ordeal, some had to be carried on a wagon to Krefeld. But they had remained true to their faith.

To their sorrow, however, they found that the Brethren church there had been split the year before. Peter Becker had led a group to Pennsylvania. One of the Solingen Brethren joined Alexander Mack in The Netherlands, but the others decided to stay in Krefeld. They did not go to America and therefore lost touch with the Brethren.

John Lobach made his home in Krefeld with his close friend, Luther Stetius. They lived by themselves in a small house. He earned his living by teaching school. They spent much time in prayer and devotions, and were noted throughout the city for their pious lives.

Lobach especially became well known because of his fine Christian life. He spent much of his time helping others — beggars, sick people, and the poor. He told them about Jesus. Although his life was a very quiet one, his influence was wide.

Once he traveled to Holland to visit Christian friends, and he visited Hochmann in Schwarzenau before the nobleman's death. He wrote many letters to friends throughout Germany and in other countries, too. What he wrote was so inspiring that people preserved his letters, and made copies of them. When they came together for worship, they would read these letters to one another.

John Lobach died in 1750. On his deathbed he told his friends to remain true to their faith. They took this request to heart, for they knew that John had shown in his own life that he had kept the faith. He had been a quiet hero for God.

— Donald F. Durnbaugh

A Patient and Courageous Leader

PETER BECKER (1687-1758)

If the leader for the Brethren families that came to America two hundred forty years ago had been chosen by an aptitude test, Peter Becker would hardly have been selected. Especially if some of the questions had been: "Are you a good public speaker? Do you stand up for your own rights? Are you a daring sailor? Have you had experience in leading people and settling in a new land?" He couldn't have said yes to any of these questions.

Perhaps he wasn't the popular kind of a man for this venture. But today the Church the Brethren honors him as the leader who organized twenty families, led them on a long and dangerous voyage to a new land, made the first missionary journeys for our church in the new world, and organized the first Church of the Brethren in America.

When we add up the score, we find this quiet man made more missionary journeys and organized more churches than any other of the early Brethren.

What is the answer?

Peter Becker was eight years younger than Alexander Mack, Sr. He was born in Düdelsheim, Germany, which was near Marienborn, where some of the Brethren came to start a fellowship. These joyful Christians had come to this place when they had to leave Schwarzenau. The way they lived was a powerful witness to thoughtful young

Becker. More and more he studied these people. He liked the way the members of this church had studied the Bible to find how they should follow Jesus. He studied his Bible. He talked to the Brethren.

"Followers of Christ," they told him, "must try to love and serve as He did. We read the story of His life in the New Testament. We take His words at face value."

"That makes sense to me," thought Peter Becker as he went back to his good farm. Day after day, as he worked, he thought about his new friends. He thought about some of the members of the Reformed church whom he had known all his life. He thought about the way they lived. He, too, had been baptized as a baby. But this did not satisfy him.

He looked lovingly at his wide fields and beautiful meadows. "Some of the Brethren have had to give up their good homes and their land for the sake of the new church," he thought. "But they seem glad that they did it. Oh, that I had their great peace!"

Perhaps Peter Becker did not talk a great deal to people, but you may be sure that he talked often to God. More important still, he listened when God spoke to him.

Finally, his mind was made up. "I want to be baptized into the Brethren church," he told his wife. "The Brethren baptize for the forgiveness of sin, in the name of the Father, and of the Son, and of the Holy Spirit. I believe that this way follows the teachings of the New Testament."

"My husband, do you not remember that Alexander Mack was made to promise not to come back to our territory? You know he will keep his promise."

"True, but I have word that John Naas will come to baptize those who feel they want baptism," answered Peter Becker.

Some of his friends tried to talk him out of taking this step. "You know our ruler is kind to those who do not agree with the state church," they pointed out. "He agrees to small groups meeting, but he does not want public baptisms. The church leaders will be angry, too. You might have to leave our community. Do not take the risk. Won't you give up the idea?"

Peter Becker slowly shook his head. "I cannot," he said thoughtfully.

"That's the way he has always been," said one disappointed friend to another. "When he was a boy, if he believed anything was right he just stuck to it no matter what."

"You know he never would say much. But I remember that when we were boys I always liked to have him on my side when we played games. I think that it was because he never bragged if we won or made excuses if we lost."

"He got more schooling than most of us, too. But that never went to his head. He is a fine fellow. I hope everything comes out all right for him."

In May 1714 Peter Becker and his wife were baptized by the Brethren.

This caused great excitement among the people of the town. "The Beckers are subjects of the count," they told one another. "What will happen now?"

"All public meetings, including baptisms, must cease," decreed Charles August, the ruler, "or the settlers will have to leave the county."

Now Peter Becker and the Brethren in the Marienborn area had to decide what to do. They talked to one another.

"Must we give up our homes again for the sake of our faith?" asked some of the settlers. "If we meet in our homes and we do not baptize we can stay here. What a pity the Inspirationists spoke publicly against our ruler and made him lose patience."

"Yes," answered others. "But if we cannot practice our belief in baptism, will our faith mean as much to us?"

The Beckers especially had much thinking to do. "This is our home," said Peter to his wife. "We have always lived here. Our friends are here. We have made a good living on our farm. I do not know what's ahead for us. For myself, I do not fear. I am thinking only of you."

"But where will we go?" asked his wife anxiously.

"We have heard," answered Peter, "that the town of Krefeld, northwest of here, near the Rhine River, is a safe place. It is one of the few places left in Germany in which the ruler is friendly."

"How would we make a living?"

"I understand that our friends the Mennonites have introduced the textile industry there. Perhaps there would be farms for sale. If we make the move, we will trust God for direction."

In the end, the decision was made to go, and Peter Becker and the other Brethren moved to Krefeld. The Brethren group began at once to witness to their faith. John Naas was their leader. The Reformed church of that area was troubled by the preaching and the baptizing of the Brethren.

"The Brethren are not only getting converts from the Mennonites," they pointed out in their meetings, "but they are getting some of the members of our own church. Something must be done!"

Something was done. Some of the Brethren were thrown into prison. Some were made to row in galley boats for years. Some gave their lives for their faith.

"These are sad days," said kind Peter Becker to the Brethren at Krefeld. "Our hearts are grieved at the sufferings of our brethren. I do not know how long we can stay here. As one of your ministers, I want you to think and pray about moving to America."

They had been hearing about that country across the ocean where land was free. But, best of all, the people there were free to worship as they wanted to.

Now another big decision was before them. Germany was their home. "If we leave," said some, "we can never return. We will have to give up everything."

"Ocean travel is hard and dangerous. Dare we risk our women and little children?"

"Is not much of the new land still a wilderness?"

Peter Becker listened. He did not wish to rush anyone. So he said, "The decision is for you to make with God's help. Let us all make it a matter for earnest prayer."

One day, Peter Becker came home with the worst news yet. His wife was almost afraid to ask why he looked so sad.

"You remember young John Höcker, who married a Mennonite girl? Well, some of the leaders wanted to make him get out of the church. Others did not. This has caused the church to be divided. The young man himself is brokenhearted. Some of the members acted as if they had forgotten about Jesus and His love." Then he added sadly, "I think we must go to America for a fresh start."

"We will go if you will be our leader," twenty families told him.

Would they have gone if they had known that the trip would take nearly six months, and that they would not have the right kind of food or even enough food? Or had they known that some of them would be sick and some would die?

When they arrived, Peter Becker said to them, "Each family will go into the home of a Mennonite family and stay until you can find homes of your own."

But he had to wait four long years for his dream of a fresh start for the church to come true. On his little farm and in his weaving shop near Germantown he must have worked and planned and prayed. "God's time is not our time," he thought.

In the fall of 1722, he and two others went to visit the Brethren who had made their homes farther out in the wilderness. They invited these Brethren to meet with them as a church again. When they returned, the group around Germantown began meeting in the homes.

In August of the following year, the people away from Germantown heard that the great preacher, Christian Liebe, had come to America.

"Let us go to hear him preach," they said.

When they came to Germantown after the long trip and found that the rumor was not true, Peter Becker talked to them. "Come, visit in my home and meet with the other Brethren," he urged kindly.

On Christmas Day of the same year, six of these people who wanted to be baptized met with the group at Germantown in the Becker home.

"We want you for our elder," the Brethren group told him.

But Peter Becker did not want to take this leadership. "I am a hymn writer and musician," he said, "and perhaps I can lead in prayer. But there are others who could lead the church better than I could."

The people insisted.

"It must be God's will," decided Peter Becker. Then he answered them in this way: "I will be your leader. But let us pray that some of the great leaders from Germany will come. Then I will give the leadership to them."

In the afternoon, they walked through the snow, single file, to the Wissahickon Creek. They read from the Bible, sang a hymn, and knelt to pray. Then Peter Becker led them, one by one, into the water and baptized them.

For six years, he was the leader of the Church of the Brethren in America. Then Alexander Mack, the founder of the church, came. "I want you to be our leader here as you were in Germany," said Becker.

After Mack's death, Peter Becker took up the burden of leadership again.

If a test for leadership had asked these questions: "Do you truly love people? Can you be patient? Do you have the courage to do what you believe is right?" Peter Becker could have answered yes to all of them.

— Mary Garber

The Grandest German of All

CHRISTOPHER SAUER, SR. (1693-1758)

So you don't know yet what you want to make your life's work? Well, don't let it get you down. While it is a relief to have your course set early in life, it does not always mean success or failure.

Take Christopher Sauer, Sr. He was thirty-seven years old, and he considered himself a failure, when he began his greatest work. In about ten years he accomplished more than most people do in a lifetime.

But he was a genius, you say? I agree. But suppose that some of the rest of us would copy his ways of doing business and his habits of work. We would do better than we do. Suppose that we lived as he did. We, too, might be called "Good Samaritans."

The motto, "To the Glory of God and My Neighbor's Good," did not hang in his shop to take up space. He lived by it! And over two centuries later his life is still an honor to the name of Sauer and to the Church of the Brethren.

Who was Christopher Sauer? He was a native German, born in 1693 in Laasphe in the County of Wittgenstein, where the ruler was friendly to religious groups who did not agree with the state church. His family was well known in the county and was able to send Christopher to school to learn many skills.

Schwarzenau was not far from his home. News didn't

travel as fast in those long-ago days, but it traveled. Christopher was greatly interested in the reports that a new church had been organized. More and more the news of the religious movement at Schwarzenau attracted him.

"I am going to move there and see for myself," he declared when he was about twenty years old, since his attendance at the Reformed church did not satisfy him.

The Brethren welcomed the young man. They answered his earnest questions about their church. "Alexander Mack and Peter Becker are my friends," he thought. "But most of all, they are God's friends. How wonderful it would be if I could always be near these dear friends. I am sure I could live a better life."

Soon Christopher Sauer realized that he wanted always to be near someone else also. She was Maria Christina Gross. They were married at Schwarzenau; and there, on September 26, 1721, Christopher, Jr., was born.

One evening, when Christopher came in later than usual from gathering herbs, he found his wife sitting by the baby's cradle, crying.

"Why, Maria, what is the matter?"

"Oh, Christopher, I thought something had happened to you. I have been so afraid."

"I am all right. And look what a fine lot of herbs I have found. Some are quite rare and they are greatly needed to make my medicines," answered the young husband, spreading out his find on the table.

"So I see," said Maria. "Christopher, do you not know there are people in our town who say you care more for your herbs and medicines than you care for your wife and baby?" And with those words Maria Sauer laid her head down on the table and sobbed as if her heart would break.

Christopher Sauer couldn't believe what he had just

heard. "But do they not know that I am trying to learn all I can, so that I can make a living in America? And that I may take some of these very herbs with us?"

"Oh, Christopher, are you still thinking of going to that faraway place? The voyage across the ocean scares me half to death. And living in a new country couldn't be as good as it is here where we have always lived."

Then Christopher Sauer spoke very seriously. "Maria, you know that Peter Becker and Alexander Mack and our other friends have had to leave this place. We do not know what may happen to us when the authorities learn that we have been their friends and that we have attended their meetings.

"These are terrible times in which to live and to try to bring up a child. Sometimes a man can hardly call his soul his own. Are not some of the people as good as owned by the ruler of this land? In America, every man has a chance. But, above all, there is blessed freedom to worship God and to follow the leading of Jesus."

"I will try to be strong, as you are," said the young wife, wiping the tears from her eyes. "Pray that God will give me faith and courage."

As soon as they reached Germantown, Christopher said, "I must find Peter Becker. I want to give him the Bible I brought him and ask his advice about a home and how to make a living."

"Come in, come in, my friends," said Peter Becker in welcome to them when they had found his home. "You must stay here until you have made plans and until you have found a place to live."

"Thank you, thank you," said Christopher Sauer. "I am more grateful than I can say. I think you know what it means to us, after those weary months on the ship."

"I do know what it means," answered Becker. "That

31

is the reason I open my home to those coming to this new land."

Christopher Sauer began to look about him for a way to earn a living. He talked to Peter Becker.

"You could stay here with me," offered his friend, "if you would be interested in the weaving business. There seems to be a future here for weaving."

Christopher Sauer shook his head, and spoke doubtfully. "I do not know the weaving business. But there are other things I can do. I have studied to be an oculist and I have studied medicine."

Just then a jolly old farmer came into the shop to see about some weaving. While he was talking to Peter Becker, Christopher Sauer was looking at him closely. Then he said,

"May I see your glasses, sir?"

"Why, certainly," laughed the farmer as he took off his broken glasses and handed them to the young man.

Christopher went to his precious chest, which he had guarded very carefully during the long voyage to America, and worked a few minutes.

"Now try them," he said to the farmer.

"Oh, thank you, thank you!" cried the owner, as he put on his glasses. "They are as good as new."

He paid Christopher Sauer and went out to spread the news that an oculist had come to Germantown. For a while there was a rush; everyone wanted his glasses repaired. Soon Christopher had time to collect herbs again. But he gave away so much medicine that he couldn't earn much. Then he decided to try tailoring, another skill he had learned in Germany. And he thought of other things he could do.

"I believe that what I would really like to do is to try farming," said Christopher Sauer to his wife one day.

"It would be nice for our son," agreed Maria.

But what the young wife did not know was that Christopher would find a farm away from Germantown, in what is now Lancaster County, Pennsylvania, and that it would be so much like her homeland that she would be homesick.

When they moved to the farm in the spring of 1726,

they were too busy to do much thinking. But when Christopher began again to make long trips for herbs, Maria was alone with the boy. She was afraid and unhappy. She thought about the strange teachings of a preacher, Conrad Beissel, and his group at nearby Ephrata.

When Christopher Sauer's wife left him and their son to join the group at Ephrata, his first thought was "I must go to my friends, Alexander Mack and Peter Becker. They will tell me what to do."

Who was Christopher Sauer?

At this point, he was a discouraged man. "I am thirty-seven years old," he said, pouring out his heart to his friends. "I consider myself a failure, not only in business but as a husband and a father. My wife has left me. I must care for my son. I do not know what to do."

"You speak and write German. Most of our people speak German. We believe God has a great work for you to do."

"What?" asked the surprised Christopher.

"What the German people need in America is a printer who is a friend to them. Benjamin Franklin does not like us Germans. He does not use the German letters when he prints in our language. You could be that friend. There should be a German Bible in every German home. Then you could branch out in your printing. Sell your farm. Come to Germantown. Put your son in school and begin this great work."

And that is just what Christopher Sauer did. At times he worked night and day. Nothing seemed to stop him. When Benjamin Franklin saw Sauer's growing business and tried to corner the paper market, Sauer bought his own paper mill. In fact, he produced nearly everything that went into the printing.

He published a newspaper, a religious magazine, and an almanac for the German people. They liked his printed works. They loved and trusted him. They even made their plans by the weather forecasts in the almanac.

One time, when a man was giving Sauer a piece of his mind because a forecast was not right, Sauer answered him, "My friend, be not so angry. It is true that I made the almanac, but the Lord Almighty made the weather."

But Christopher Sauer's greatest work was the printing of the first German Bible in America. This he did

34

with a hand press. Only four pages could be printed at a time. It took more than a year to complete it. After it was finished, on a hot July night, the great man gathered his workmen about him, folded his arms, turned his eyes toward heaven, and exclaimed, "Thank God, it is finished!"

Who was Christopher Sauer?

"Let us tell you," answered the poor people who came to America on overcrowded ships and who were often treated worse than animals. "He took us into his home, he doctored us, he gave us food and clothes, and he helped us get started in the new world. He was the 'Good Samaritan' of Germantown."

He was the grandest German of all.

— Mary Garber

Another Noble Sauer

CHRISTOPHER SAUER, JR. (1721-1784)

One dark night during the Revolutionary War, rough soldiers entered a fine brick house in Germantown, Pennsylvania, and dragged from his bed a fifty-six-year-old Church of the Brethren minister, a leading and well-known citizen of Pennsylvania. They made him hurry through a cornfield to an old barn. When he stumbled and fell, the soldiers cursed him and struck him with their bayonets.

At the barn they made him take off his clothes and put on an old torn shirt and worn-out trousers. They cut off his hair and his beard. They painted his body with red and black oil colors. Then they forced him to march many miles, without hat or shoes, in the hot sun, to their camp.

On the way a friend saw the cruel treatment. He wanted to give the minister his hat and shoes. "Will you let him keep them?" he asked.

"He can keep them," the soldiers promised. But after a few miles, one soldier took the shoes and gave the minister his old ones, which hurt his feet very much.

At the camp, the soldiers dragged him before their commanding officer and accused him of being a spy and a traitor to his country.

But a general, who knew and admired Christopher Sauer, Jr., sent him the word, "Appeal to General Washington." Sauer did, and Washington set him free at once.

Not long after Christopher Sauer returned home, officials came and took nearly everything he owned and sold it. They seized his house, his printing presses, his ink factory, and his farms.

"Please let me keep some of my medicines," Sauer begged.

"Certainly not. Medicines are valuable" was the rude reply. And they sold everything the wealthy man owned, except his spectacles!

Christopher Sauer lived when times were very difficult for the Brethren in America. It was a period of change and unrest. There was fighting between England and her American colonies. And there had recently been the French and Indian wars. The peace-loving Quakers no longer ruled in Pennsylvania, and the Germans — Mennonites, Brethren, and others — were no longer welcome in the colony.

To understand Christopher Sauer, Jr., and his experiences which have been told above, we shall need to look at his life up until the time of the Revolutionary War.

He was born in his father's home town in Germany. At the age of three years he had been brought to Pennsylvania by his parents. When he was nine years old, at the time the family was living on a farm in Lancaster County, his mother left home. She had the strange beliefs taught by Conrad Beissel, and had gone to live in the Ephrata Cloister. Instead of adding to his father's burden by wanting all his attention, young Christopher gave him love and understanding. And he never gave up hope that his mother would someday return to her family.

"I know Mother will come back to us sometime," he told his father many times. "I will keep on writing and asking her to come." It was a letter which he wrote to her after he had become a young man that finally caused her to decide to go back to her family after fourteen years in the Cloister. By that time the Sauers were living in Germantown, near Philadelphia.

Soon after Christopher and his father moved to Germantown, he was enrolled in the school of a very strict schoolmaster, the famous Christopher Dock. There he made good use of his opportunities to learn. "If your son continues his habits of study," the schoolmaster told the elder Sauer, "he will be one of the best educated men in the American colonies."

While his son was in school, Christopher Sauer, Sr., worked as hard as he could in his printing shop. The boy early took an interest in the shop and spent much of his out-of-school time working there. By the time he was sixteen, he could do very well at bookbinding. Some of the boys his age could not understand his interest in the shop. "Why do you work in that old shop?" they would say. "It will be yours someday. Then there will be time for you to work in it. Come on out and have some fun." But Christopher kept on working. He also took long walks with his father to find herbs for medicine. He was constantly asking questions. He was listening carefully as his father shared his knowledge with him.

When Christopher, Jr., was fifteen years old, he told his father that he wanted to be baptized into the Church of the Brethren.

His father listened kindly and carefully, as he always did no matter how busy he was. "My son, you are young for a decision. Our leaders usually suggest that one wait until he is older. But it seems to me that you are certain in your mind now. I suggest you talk to our elder, Peter Becker."

Thus, early in life Christopher Sauer, Jr., accepted

Jesus as Lord and Master of his life. "I will try to follow His teachings," he vowed, "come what may."

He loved the church. He was a beloved leader. He was called to the ministry. Wherever this forceful minister preached, the principles of the Church of the Brethren were better understood and respected and the church grew. He used the powerful Sauer press to attack the evils of war and slavery. He spoke out in plain words, even though he made many enemies in so doing. He tested problems and questions by the life and teachings of Jesus as he found them in the New Testament. Then he stuck to what he believed was right. Perhaps no leader of the Brethren has ever followed more closely the example and the teachings of Jesus than did Christopher Sauer, Jr.

He became the best friend the German people in America had, as his father had been in his day. And they badly needed friends! It was hard enough to begin life in a strange country. But not knowing the language made it much harder still. Often, they would get into trouble simply because they could not read or speak English and they could not understand what was expected of them.

The Sauer printers discussed this situation. "I believe," said the elder Sauer to his son, "that the future of America belongs to the English and their language. But most of our people still cling to their German ways and the German language. We could help them change to the American culture."

"Do you mean we should do more printing in the English language?"

"Yes, that is what I have in mind. But I think we should continue to serve the German people. Many of them are old, as I am. They will probably never learn a new language. I could continue the German printing. On the other hand, the younger people are learning English. You speak and write the English language well. You could take over the work of publishing English books."

"We would still work together, wouldn't we?" asked the younger Sauer quickly.

"Just as always, my son," his father assured him. "But change must come. I believe the time has come for our people to begin to change to the English culture. We must change our business. Then, the time has come for you to begin to take more responsibility, while I would like to have less. But let us never change our motto, 'To the Glory of God and My Neighbor's Good.' Let us honor God in all we do, and let us serve those of our fellow men who need us."

"Thank you for your faith in me, Father," said Christopher, Jr. "What you have begun well, I will carry on the best that I can. I will try not to disappoint you."

"You never have," quietly answered his father.

The two men continued to work side by side as long as Sauer, Sr., was able to work. All the while Christopher, Jr., was pushing out in his own right. His father had printed one edition of the Bible; he printed two. He improved his father's newspaper. He enlarged the paper mills and set up the first type foundry in the colonies.

But he did not give all his time to printing. He was interested in good roads and good streets. He was one of the founders and trustees of the Germantown Academy. He was a good friend and helper of the German immigrants when they arrived in Philadelphia. Often they had lost everything they owned on the voyage and were sick when they reached Philadelphia. He helped so many of them and others as well that he became known as the "Bread Father of Germantown."

Above all he was a churchman. For many years he served the Germantown church as its pastor and elder. At one time after the war and the loss of his printing presses, Annual Conference appointed him to visit all the churches in Pennsylvania. And two weeks before his death, it is said, he walked twelve miles to preach.

When, in 1777, the government of Pennsylvania passed a law that all citizens must transfer their allegiance from the king of England to the Commonwealth of Pennsylvania by taking the oath, Sauer said, "I cannot do it. I can affirm my loyalty to my government. But my Bible says, 'Swear not at all.' I cannot take an oath." Perhaps his refusal was just the excuse that some jealous and wicked persons were wanting to permit them to seize his press and his other property.

"I am not sorry I chose the path of peace," said Christopher Sauer, Jr., to his friend, Alexander Mack, Jr., when Mack went to visit him. "My printing presses, my home, and all my property are gone. My children are scattered. But I have the peace of God in my heart. And He still has work for me to do!"

Who could say that Christopher Sauer, Jr., lost everything, when he had lived up to his ideals?

— *Mary Garber*

A Brethren Frontiersman

GEORGE WOLFE, JR. (1780-1865)

"Jump out, boys. We want to finish that flatboat today." Elder Wolfe's voice carried clearly into the loft where his sons were sleeping.

George, Jr., and his brother Jacob did not wait for the second call. In one motion they threw back the warm comforts and jumped out of bed.

"We'll finish that boat and start another one before the day is over," George declared, reaching for his homespun shirt.

"It's likely we will," agreed Jacob, rescuing his woolen socks from under the bed. "With three boats sold and only one finished we'll need to work faster than a woodpecker pecks."

"Spring will be here like the snap of your finger," George answered. "According to the almanac, today is February 1, 1800. And listen, Jacob" — George lowered his voice — "if you're still counting on going to Kentucky I'm going along."

"I'm going," said Jacob. "But I'm hoping Father and Mother and Ann will go too."

George, twenty years old, six feet tall, broad shouldered, strong limbed, and quick in his movements, swung down the ladder and dropped to the floor below. Jacob, three years older, followed with the same quick skill.

While the family was seated at breakfast, Father

Wolfe read from his German Bible of Abram going to a far country. George and Jacob exchanged glances. Being a Brethren preacher, their father usually read from the New Testament. Mother Wolfe caught the meaning of the reading too.

After the blessing she spoke. "We left our church home once and came into a far country. And a terrible risk it was."

"But a good move," Father answered. "We've been blessed here in western Pennsylvania."

"I remember when we moved from Lancaster County and came here to the Monongahela River," George said, reaching for the maple syrup. "I was seven years old. To cross the mountains in a wagon was a great adventure."

"It's my purpose to adventure for God," declared Father Wolfe as Mother handed him a hot corn scone. "I've preached New Testament sermons all over this part of the country. I think it's time for me to preach to those who have not yet heard of our beliefs. We are going to build a boat for the Wolfes, too. Come the proper time and we will ride the river to Kentucky."

George let out a whoop of joy. With his blue eyes shining and his untrimmed, red-brown hair hanging long from his fur cap, he left the house to pick up his tools and go to work.

The flatboats built and sold by the Wolfes were stout and well worth the seventy-five dollars charged for them. Elder Wolfe was fair to his sons and paid them rightful wages for their shares.

Throughout that spring of 1800, George's mind worked as fast as his hands. "I'm going to buy land with my money," he told Jacob. "Lots of land."

It was also George who worked hard at learning to speak and read English. Growing up in the wilderness had deprived the Wolfe children of school privileges. Their father and mother had clung to their German language and read their German Bible. George learned English from the many English-speaking people whom he met. He practiced reading from *Poor Richard's Almanac*.

At last the Wolfes had completed their own boat. It lay on the river, fifty feet long and fourteen feet wide. Its snug cabin was furnished with Mother Wolfe's house-keeping things. It was stored with ample provisions.

A team of horses and other livestock were given a place on one end of the craft. Farming and timber tools and their woodsmen's rifles were properly on board.

"Shove off, boys," Elder Wolfe shouted as he untied the boat and jumped on board.

George and Jacob bent to the sweeps. Slowly the boat moved out into the stream, while their friends stood on shore waving good-by to this family they would never see again.

"God be with you," they called.

"God bless you," came the answer from the boat.

"Ah!" thought George. "This is good."

But the trip was a dangerous one, even for these men who were skilled on the river and in the woods. The country was beautiful but the water was high; the Indians were hostile and the white settlements were few and far between.

Each evening the Wolfes tied their craft in a sheltered place. Each morning the Bible lesson was read and thanks were given to God. Then again they turned out into the stream. It was weeks before they reached the Green River, a hundred miles southwest of Louisville. There they turned south into Kentucky.

Somewhere the Wolfes sold their flatboat and by team and wagon drove into Muhlenberg and Logan counties.

"This is good country, Father," George said at last.

"I agree," his father answered. "And these Brethren we've met here are rightly taught although they are English from North Carolina. I've a notion to stay."

"I know I'm staying," George said, thinking of pretty Anna Hunsaker, whose parents were Brethren from North Carolina.

It was March 3, 1803, when George Wolfe, Jr., and Anna Hunsaker were married. But George had not yet found the land he wished to buy. He had heard of the wild hills and the prairies of the Illinois country, with no white men there excepting the French on the Mississippi.

Into that unknown land George Wolfe and Abram Hunsaker went as explorers in the late fall of 1803.

"This is what I've been looking for," George said, his eyes glowing with a vision of the future. "Here are game, timber, water, and rich soil. I'm going to build a cabin right now."

By 1808 three young couples from the Brethren families in Kentucky had selected their land and moved their families into Illinois, forty miles north of the point later to be known as Cairo. They were George and Jacob Wolfe and their wives and Ann Wolfe, who had married Abram Hunsaker. Strange to say, not one had been baptized into the Brethren faith.

"Did you bring your Bible, Anna?" George asked one evening. "We have plenty of bear tallow for candles and I don't want to forget how to read English."

"It's in my chest," Anna said, going to bring the precious book. "And I reckon we'd better not forget its teachings, either. You read and I'll listen while I knit. And mind you, no German accent."

There was a terrible earthquake along the Mississippi River in 1811. After that there was a rush of settlers into

Illinois areas. Soon the Wolfes had several neighbors. A few months later a Methodist preacher rode into their community and preached powerful Methodist sermons. Fourteen people were converted and formed a class to study the creed and prepare for baptism. George Wolfe, now thirty-two years old, was appointed leader of the class.

Anna noticed that her husband was unusually thoughtful and that he was reading chapter after chapter in the New Testament.

He surprised her by saying, at the first meeting, "Brethren and sisters, I've pondered and prayed over this matter and I conclude that if John Wesley is the Savior we are right. But if Jesus Christ is the Savior we are wrong."

It was a shocking thought.

"What must we do?" the others asked after much discussion.

"I suggest," said George, "that we send to Kentucky for a Brethren preacher to come to us."

This was done, and, as a result, the class of fourteen were baptized and became the first Brethren in Illinois. In 1813 George Wolfe was properly ordained as a Brethren preacher.

History was being made and the influence of George Wolfe moved powerfully in civic affairs as well as in the church, in which he soon became an elder.

If he was preaching in the log meetinghouse, or if he was sitting on the grand jury in the log courthouse, he was honest and just.

If he was advising a senator, or consulting with the governor, or debating with a Catholic priest, or speaking against slavery, his logic and his language were those of an educated person.

If he was looking after his seven hundred fifty acres

46

of land, or performing a wedding ceremony, or branding his cattle, or reproving an erring person, his kindness and wisdom won him honor and respect. Then, too, there was often the twinkling of his eyes that showed his kindly sense of humor.

As the years went by, George Wolfe made each day count.

"Where are you going today, Father," one of the children might ask.

It might have been to Missouri, or to Indiana, or to nearby Bald Knob to preach, or to conduct a love feast, or to hold a funeral.

At last times changed in southern Illinois.

"Many of our Brethren have moved north to Adams County," George said one evening in 1831. "Should we go too?"

"I keep thinking of it," Anna answered, laying her sewing aside. "Half of the large landowners here are slaveholders. I don't like the situation."

"Nor I," George said, laying a log on the fire. He stood on the hearth, a majestic, middle-aged man. "My father once said that it was his purpose to adventure for God. That has become my purpose too, Anna. I am a pioneer. I can work better in a new country with new people. We'll move."

After George had moved his wife and eight children to Adams County, he soon became a familiar figure in west-central Illinois. He rode here and there preaching from the New Testament. He used gentle but commanding persuasion. The people loved to listen and many were baptized.

He went to Governor Reynolds at the outbreak of the Black Hawk War, explaining the Brethren belief about peace and war.

"Return to your home," said Governor Reynolds. "We need men of peace." And he handed Elder Wolfe a paper exempting all Brethren from military service.

In later years this question was often asked: "Did you know George Wolfe?"

"Yes," said the ferryman at Naples on the Illinois River. "I ferried that man and his horse across the river each year for twenty-five years. You can't forget a man like him."

"Yes," said the historians who were writing the history of the state. "George Wolfe was a pioneer preacher of great power, familiar in his flat, black hat and his great cape-coat, with his long beard flowing over his chest."

"Yes," said the Brethren. "And we remember his words spoken in 1864 at the district meeting of Southern Illinois. He said, 'I came to the church. I weighed well her doctrines, her rules, and her orders. I joined her communion because I loved her. I turned away from the world. I reasoned that I did not love the world, but I loved the church. I will not be like the world I hate but will be like the church I love.'"

George Wolfe, born April 25, 1780, died November 16, 1865. Like Paul, he had finished his work. Like the good servant, he was ready for the words, "Well done."

— Ethel H. Weddle

The First Brethren Woman Preacher

SARAH RIGHTER MAJOR (1808-1884)

"My child, what is troubling you?" asked John Righter, a Brethren minister, of his daughter, Sarah.

Sarah only shook her head. She could not, she just could not, tell anyone, not even her father, what was in her heart.

However, her father did not give up. "Sarah, I know something is making you very unhappy. Won't you tell your father? I want to try to help you."

Because love is stronger than anything else, the young girl soon found herself telling her father all about it, a little at a time.

"I want to be a preacher," she ventured. Then she waited for his disapproval. When it failed to come, she risked a look at her father's face. It was kind and tender. Then she went on. "Ever since I heard the great Harriet Livermore preach and I joined the church, I have felt a call in my heart to preach. But I have been afraid to tell anyone. I know our church will not like a woman preacher."

"I know how you must feel, my daughter," answered John Righter, "because there are no women preachers in the Church of the Brethren. But remember this: You never need be ashamed of wanting to tell others about Christ. However, we want to do this in the right way. I believe that we should ask the advice of our good and wise elder, Peter Keyser. He will tell us what to do."

The busy man welcomed the father and the daughter, and said to her, "Sarah, I was very glad that you were baptized into our church here in Philadelphia. It does my heart good to see the young people coming into the church. They are the hope for the future. They have the energy to work. And they have many years to serve the Lord. How old are you, my child?"

"I am eighteen, sir," answered Sarah, "and, oh, how much I want to serve my church!"

Her father helped her. "Sarah feels a call in her heart to work for God as a preacher. But we know that some people will not like a woman preacher. We have come to ask your advice."

"I do not believe Jesus ever spoke against a woman serving as a preacher," said Elder Keyser, who knew all of the New Testament and much of the Old Testament by memory. He could quote whole chapters, not missing a single word. He himself was a great preacher. But here he was encouraging a young person to preach — and a girl at that! "If God calls one for a special task, you may be sure He will be with you, even if some people do not understand and they say unkind things."

So it came about that young Sarah Righter began her public ministry in her home church in Philadelphia. Some people found fault and spoke out against her. But Sarah expected this and kept straight on her way, sure of her call.

Because she had the courage to preach and the will to live her sermons, the church accepted women preachers. Today, the Church of the Brethren lists over sixty women preachers in the *Yearbook*.

The church at Amwell, New Jersey, soon invited Sarah Righter to visit and to preach. She spoke such humble and helpful messages that her field of service grew rapidly.

"Come out to hear Sarah Righter and you will change your mind about women preachers," people said to those who stayed away. And when they did come they forgot the woman as they listened to the gospel message she brought.

Wherever she went, Sarah Righter was invited to come again. She never pushed herself forward, but waited to be invited to speak. Men as well as women liked to hear her.

Perhaps the greatest work this pioneering Brethren woman did was done after she married Thomas Major, also a Brethren minister.

This marriage was an interesting subject to some women of the neighborhood who were visiting one afternoon. "Do you suppose Sarah Major will try to keep on preaching, since she has a husband and a home to care for?" asked the hostess.

"Well, I do not see how she could," declared her neighbor. "If she has as much work to do as I have, she will hardly be able to get to church, much less do any preaching."

"And she is starting a home late in life, too. She is thirty-four, isn't she? She will soon find out what a big job it is, I'm afraid."

"Sarah Major strikes me as a woman who is able to do big things," said a third, who had been listening quietly. "You remember that when she was a young girl she went right on answering God's call to preach, in spite of the fact that there were no women preachers and some people did not like what she was doing. I am sure she can continue to do it and care for her home, too."

"I do not suppose we will know the answer to our

question, for I hear that the Majors have sold their farm and are moving to Highland County, Ohio," concluded the hostess.

Her husband, her three children, her neighbors, those in need all about her, and the churches of Ohio and Indiana could answer that question. She served her home, her community, and her church in a wonderful way.

"Of a truth," said Sarah Major, "if God calls one for a special task, He will give the strength and the courage to do it."

— Mary Garber

Missionary to the Red Man

ADAM PAYNE (1780-1832)

Not a person moved. Not a leaf stirred. Even the wind seemed to be holding its breath. There was no sound in the Indian council of war, except the voice of the tall black-haired, black-bearded Brethren preacher.

"I am the prophet of the Great Spirit," he declared, his voice ringing out in the stillness. "My great Master is the Prince of Peace. He does not want His children to fight each other."

Adam Payne stood on a log with his open Bible held high in one hand. "The words of the Great Spirit are in this Book," he said. "He loves both the white man and the Indian. He wants us to live together in peace. The land and the rivers are enough for both. Put away your plans for war. Let us live in peace. Let us have 'peace on earth, goodwill to men.'"

This man so stirred the Indians that some of them cried out, "Let us bury the hatchet. Let us live in peace with the white man."

But all the time this preacher was pleading for the Indians not to go to war with the white man, a sullen and powerful Indian chief was seated on the ground, listening to every word. He was Black Hawk, chief of the Sauk and Fox tribes. His eyes never left the white man's face. As soon as Payne finished talking, this great Indian warrior jumped up and began to speak against

Payne and his plea for peace. No other Indian could stir his people as Black Hawk did. No other Indian could speak like Black Hawk.

"We could band together," he cried, "and drive the white men from our land. There is no room in Illinois for white men and Indians. They took our lands and our rivers. Where will we hunt and fish? They destroyed our graves, which are sacred to us. The mother will go alone to weep over the grave of her child. The brave, with pleasure, visits the grave of his father, after he has been successful in war. There is left to us no place like that, where the bones of our forefathers lie, to go to when in grief."

Soon the braves began to mutter and to agree with Black Hawk. The Indian warrior was beginning to have things his way, and he knew it. It looked as if the hundreds of Indian braves might turn against this Brethren preacher, whom they had known and respected. The Indian war cry might be heard any moment. The turning point was near. What would happen?

But in the council of war there was also an old and wise Indian chief who stood up and said, "I have seen all of war that I care to see. It is not good. I believe that the red man and the paleface should try to live together in peace as the white man has said."

This was it! The council decided against going to war with the white man. Black Hawk left, a disappointed and angry man.

All of this happened on July 1, 1830, in Bureau County, Illinois, about twenty miles south of Dixon. Many events in the lives of the Indians and of Adam Payne had been leading up to it. We must look at a few of them.

This was not the first time a Brethren preacher, in

those days, had spoken to a group seated on the ground even if it was the first time one had spoken at an Indian war council. The pioneer congregations often met under trees when the weather was warm. Sometimes they gathered in homes or in schoolhouses. On the frontier there were no beautiful church buildings like those we have today. But now the place where the Indian council was held is no longer a frontier. Some of our most beautiful farming lands and cities are in Illinois and Wisconsin. And there are many churches of the Brethren there, which were started by Adam Payne and other brave pioneer preachers.

Brave? Did you think that only soldiers were brave? Pioneer preachers would top the list of brave men. There were no fast trains, airplanes, buses, or cars to make traveling easy. These men walked or they rode horses. They traveled through mud and snow. Sometimes the horses had to swim muddy rivers. They could not ride up to a fine motel and secure lodging. They stopped for the night at a lonely cabin or slept out in the open, always knowing that wild animals or unfriendly Indians might be near. Their one thought seemed to be to carry the gospel to those who had not heard it and to minister to those who had accepted Jesus as their Lord.

Adam Payne wanted the Indians, too, to know the story of Jesus and His love. Many times he took with him a half-breed Indian to act as an interpreter.

They were indeed a strange pair. The preacher was tall, black-eyed and black-haired, with a winning smile. Mike Girty, the Indian, was cruel and savage looking. One loved God and all his fellow men. The other did not. That fact made all the difference in the world.

"You are my friend," the Brethren minister told his interpreter. "I trust you."

"I will be true to you," answered Mike Girty. And he was.

On their trips through northern Illinois and southern Wisconsin they camped at night along the Indian trails. The Indian could quickly choose the best spot and set up camp. After the meal, while they sat by the campfire, Adam Payne would sometimes sing. He was a good singer and his beautiful voice carried out into the stillness of the night. They could look up through the trees and see the heavens God created. Each man, in his own way, would think of God. And Mike Girty's face would lose some of its savage look.

At other times his savage look was plain, especially when they talked of the coming of the white man to Indian lands.

Many white men and Indians could not understand each other, but this Brethren preacher could see the side of the red man, too. The Indians loved and trusted him for it. He was known throughout the Indian country and he was not afraid to go anywhere, because he was a friend to the Indians. But, most white men and Indians were not friends.

Adam Payne and Mike Girty talked about the growing trouble.

"The Treaty of 1804, that was signed in St. Louis," said Adam Payne, "gave the white man the eastern third of Missouri and the land lying between the Wisconsin, Fox, Illinois, and Mississippi rivers, didn't it? The white man was to pay the Indian $1,000 a year, and the Indian could hunt and fish as always, until the land was needed for settlement."

"White man has pushed into Indian country," declared Girty. "He is land grabber. He plows over Indian burying ground."

"I know that Black Hawk, the chief of the Sauk and Fox tribes, says he was deceived by the treaty terms in St. Louis. And perhaps he was. It does seem that the price for the land was not fair. But we must come to an understanding. We must not fight."

"Black Hawk is very angry," answered the half-breed. "Some Indians have crossed the Mississippi River and left their land. Black Hawk says he will not go. He will fight white man and drive him from Indian country."

"No, no," said the preacher of peace. "We must not fight. We must live in peace. There is room for all."

But Black Hawk was a great leader. He was the kind of man who could get people to follow him. He was a restless, hot-tempered warrior, who never trusted the white man. He was greatly disturbed by the coming of a people whom he did not like and whom he did not understand. He brooded over the wrong he thought was done his people. He talked to other chiefs. And he planned. He kept talking and planning.

Finally, the great Indian feast was set at which both Adam Payne and Black Hawk stirred the Indians by their great power as speakers.

Black Hawk left the council of war quickly, when the Indians decided not to fight. He was angry and insulted. "I will get even," he vowed. "I will drive the white man from Indian country. He is enemy."

You can read in your history books about the dreadful Black Hawk War. Many white people and many Indians lost their lives. History would have been different if the Indian warrior had believed the wise old chief and the Brethren preacher that day at the war council.

Following the council, Adam Payne went to Dixon, then known as Dixon Ferry. This was the military headquarters for the northern part of the state. Here the army officers, Jefferson Davis, Zachary Taylor, and Abraham Lincoln, were busy recruiting and training soldiers to fight the Indians. There had already been one Indian uprising. Everyone was excited. "War may break out any minute," they said. "We must be ready."

What did Preacher Payne do? He just kept on preaching the gospel of peace to the white man and to the Indian! "We must not fight," he urged. "We can understand each other."

The Brethren minister was free to go among the Indians as well as the white people. He was loved and trusted by both sides. But it was becoming more and more dangerous.

In early May 1832, Adam Payne held a service at what is now the corner of Water Street and Michigan Avenue in Chicago. He kept his audience standing for two hours while he preached. Then he mounted his horse to ride away.

"Do not go," urged the people. "The Indians are on the warpath in the western part of the state. Stay here until things quiet down."

"The Indians know and respect me," the preacher assured them. "I have no fear."

In the afternoon of May 23, 1832, Payne was riding slowly along an Indian trail, when all at once three rifle shots rang out. One bullet struck the horse, which soon fell. The Indians then rushed upon the Brethren minister and killed him, while he stood with uplifted Bible.

The missionary to the Indians gave his life for what he believed. The message he preached has lived on and on in the hearts of his fellow men, changing lives and bringing them into the Kingdom of God.

— *Mary Garber*

Our Greatest Historian

Abraham Cassel (1820-1908)

"Of course you cannot go to school! Why do you think you need to? Your father and your mother never went to school. And we have gotten along very well."

This was the answer that young Abraham Cassel received when he asked his father if he might attend school when the farm work was laid by in the fall.

"But, Father, I want to learn to read."

This stern Pennsylvania German father looked hard at his oldest son.

"What is the matter with you anyway, Son? The other children do not bother me this way. If you learn to read, you will just waste your time. And you would read things that it would be better for you not to know. I will have no more of this talk about going to school. There is enough work on the farm to keep us busy."

Perhaps there was no more talk about school from the boy at that time. But there was a great deal of thinking going on in his alert mind. He wanted to go to school. He wanted it more than anything else. In his mind there was a deep hunger for knowledge. There were many questions to which he wanted to know the answers. If only he could read he could find some of them.

The whole situation simply did not make sense to young Abraham. Why was his father so set against his going to school? Why had his father and his mother not learned to read and write? Why did some of the other Brethren in Montgomery County, Pennsylvania, where he lived, not let their children go to school? How could it be a sin to learn to read?

Slowly, some of his questions began to clear up in his thinking. "My mother," he thought, "is the granddaughter of Christopher Sauer and of Peter Becker. They were educated men. They were great leaders in the Church of the Brethren. They are remembered and honored for their good lives. Something has happened to the Brethren that they no longer want to be educated. Learning is not a sin. It can be used for good, with God's help. I am going to learn."

And he did! But it was anything but easy. He had to keep on doing hard work on his father's farm. It was never easy to do enough work to please his father, who thought his farm work was of the greatest importance.

But Abraham was the kind of a boy who did not give up. His sister taught him to spell. His Uncle George showed him how to shape a feather and use it for a pen. And how do you suppose he learned to read? By using a small picturebook. Since his father would not even let him have a candle, he had to try to find some time during the day for reading — when his father was not aware of it.

Now comes a real believe-it-or-not. Although Abraham Cassel went to regular school only six weeks, he became the greatest historian the Church of the Brethren has ever had. Scholars from all over the world came to his wonderful library for information that could not be found anywhere else.

Further, after many years of studying by himself, he learned enough to become a schoolteacher. How happy he must have been, since he had deeply wanted to go to school himself, to be able to teach boys and girls some of the things he had had to learn under the most unpleasant circumstances.

It was while he was teaching school that he thought still more about the work of his great-grandfathers, Christopher Sauer and Peter Becker. They were both important leaders in the Church of the Brethren; and yet, many people did not remember them and their great work.

"These great men should not be forgotten," he said to his wife, Elizabeth. "You know, since I was a child I have been saving all the books, papers, and pamphlets that I could find. I have some of their writings and some facts about the early church. But there must be much valuable information in old books in people's attics."

"We can save somewhere else," answered his wife, "and I am sure that if we offer a good price we can get many rare books."

Abraham Cassel's famous library grew and grew until it reached fifty thousand books and papers. This was before the Dewey Decimal System was devised for libraries; but he used his own methods to arrange his library so that all the material could be easily found. Today, most of this great library is at Juniata College at Huntingdon, Pennsylvania.

Wouldn't it have been fun to visit Abraham Cassel's library? We might have met John Greenleaf Whittier gathering material for his poem, *The Pennsylvania Pilgrim,* or Governor Martin G. Brumbaugh writing his book, *A History of the German Baptist Brethren,* or famous people from other countries.

But most of all, this library was a source of great enjoyment for Abraham Cassel. Now he could read all he wanted to and he could share his books with others.

— Mary Garber

Printer of Our First Church Paper

HENRY KURTZ (1796-1874)

"Hunt out what people need most and forget all about your own comfort while you try to give it to them." That is the way to find God, says Frank Laubach, known throughout our world today for his efforts to teach people to read.

That is exactly what Henry Kurtz did when he printed a church paper for Brethren to read, over one hundred years ago. He saw that the church needed a magazine. He forgot about his own comfort and tried to give the church what it needed. God was with him. And Henry Kurtz is known today as the pioneer of modern printing in the Church of the Brethren.

For seventy-five years after the printing press, the home, and other property of Christopher Sauer, Jr., were seized because he refused to take part in war or to take the oath of allegiance to the Commonwealth of Pennsylvania, the Church of the Brethren had no printing plant and no publications.

During these years, also, the Brethren became quite scattered. Some of them moved west and some of them moved into the southern states. They could no longer go to the same churches or visit and talk about their problems together. Few could attend the Annual Meetings. They had no church paper or quarterlies to guide them. No wonder that they became confused in their ideas! What one church thought was right to do, another church thought was wrong.

At the Annual Meeting of 1848 there was so much business brought before the meeting that the clerk of the Conference, Henry Kurtz, could sense that the situation was getting worse and worse.

"We need a church paper," he declared to his friend and elder, George Hoke. "A church paper would help our people understand each other. In it we could exchange ideas and news. It would help unite our Brethren who are now living so far apart."

"Yes," answered Elder Hoke. "There is great need for something to hold our people together. They have been spreading out over our whole country."

Henry Kurtz became more eager and excited. "I think about it most of the time," he exclaimed.

"I believe," said Elder Hoke slowly, "that our people are ready for such a step now."

"I think so, too," agreed Henry.

"Henry Kurtz, you are the man to start such a paper," declared George Hoke.

"It is what I want more than anything else," he said. "But I have failed two times. The Brethren would not buy subscriptions."

"That is true" was the answer. "But you have waited until more people are ready for such a step. You believe that the church needs a paper. I believe that God sent you to us for such a time as this. You have had much experience as clerk of the Annual Meeting. You know the condition of the church as well as anyone else does. You have more education than most of us. Many of our people still speak German. You understand both English and German. Since you have not always been a Brethren minister, perhaps you would have a broader viewpoint on our problems. More than that, you have learned the printing trade and you have a printing press."

"God helping me, I will try again," said Henry Kurtz.

Not only did *he* try. But so also did his wife and his children. Soon they were having a family conference to plan how they could do it.

First, the father told them how greatly the church needed a paper. "Some of the Brethren act as if they have forgotten how to read," he said. "They act as if farm work was more important than anything else. Some boys and girls do not have anything at all to read. I want to print a church paper on our press in the old springhouse loft. And I want all of you to help me."

It was decided that two of the boys would help their father with the printing, while the other two sons would do the farm work. Of course, all hands would help at harvesttime on the farm. Everybody had a job. Everybody worked hard.

Even then it was not easy. Brother Kurtz did most of the writing and editing in his farmhouse sitting room at night while others slept. When set in type, the pages were run off on the hand press in the springhouse loft. Then the edition was hauled five miles over mud roads to the post office. An editor in those days must also know how to set type, read the proofs, make up the forms, operate the press, and handle the mailing. Sounds like a full-time job, doesn't it? Editor Kurtz also had the oversight of the Poland church and operated his farm. How did he do it all? A tracing of his life up to this time will help to answer that question.

Henry Kurtz was born in Germany in 1796. His father was an educated man and spent part of his time teaching. He was a faithful Lutheran.

"My son," he said, "get all the education you can.

I am happy that you are thinking of becoming a minister. It would be fine if you studied Hebrew, Latin, and Greek."

When Henry Kurtz was twenty-one years old, he came to the United States. Like his father, he too became a teacher. But it was only to earn a living while he studied for what he really wanted to be, a Lutheran minister.

As a pastor, he took his first charge in 1819. Very soon after that, he took a wife. Her name was Anna Catharine Loehr. In 1820, he went to the Lutheran church in Pittsburgh, Pennsylvania, as its pastor.

It was while he was here that there came a turning point in his life, for which the Church of the Brethren should be forever grateful.

Often he discussed his thoughts with his wife. "The more I read my Bible," he said, "and the more I see the lives of those about me, the more I believe that faith is necessary for true baptism."

"And some understanding and some experience are necessary for faith, aren't they?" replied Anna Catharine. "But babies have neither one, and our church practices infant baptism."

"It is becoming very disturbing to me. Every time I baptize a baby, I feel that it is not the right thing to do. I am going to speak out against this doctrine."

It made quite a stir among the Lutherans when Pastor Kurtz opposed infant baptism.

The people naturally took sides. Some wanted to throw him out of the church — the sooner the better. Had not infant baptism always been one of the doctrines of the church? Who did this young pastor think he was?

There were others who were different. "Let us go slow," they said. "We have a fine young pastor here. He has done much for our church. Where could we find a better preacher? And his prayers mean so much, not only in the pulpit, but at the bedside of our sick. All of us like to hear him sing and play on the organ. And what about the little German monthly paper he prints? Our young

people and older people enjoy that. It keeps them in touch with other members of the church. Could we not bear with him awhile and see what happens?"

But some people just cannot wait. They talked so long and loud that Pastor Kurtz was finally expelled.

Take a look. Here was a young man, trained to be a minister, with a wife and a family to support. But he had no church in which to work.

As Henry Kurtz looked back at this event and the years that followed, he saw that truly the hand of God was in his life. Let no one pretend it was easy. It must have taken every bit of his courage and faith to keep working and to keep seeking the truth.

It was after he was located on a farm in northeastern Ohio, where he also did some printing for others, that Henry Kurtz heard of the Brethren. He began to attend their meetings. He listened; he studied; he asked questions. Under the great preaching of Elder George Hoke, he decided that the Church of the Brethren beliefs were his beliefs. "I want to be baptized," he said.

Not long after being baptized he was ordained into the ministry. From this time on, he was very active in church work. He was given the care of the Poland church, a charge he kept for thirty years. He also visited other churches to preach. He nearly always attended Annual Conference, serving as clerk for fifteen years.

However, all this time he was dreaming of another need of his beloved Church of the Brethren — the need for a church paper.

He thought about it. He prayed about it. He talked about it. "Our people," he said, "need more reading materials in their homes. Some homes which I have visited have only the Bible to read. Young people, especially, are eager to read."

Brother Kurtz understood how it was before many other people understood. He was that kind of man.

"We are afraid someone would publish something we do not like," some objected. "Besides, who wants to spend good money for such things as papers?"

But Brother Kurtz was also the kind of man who would not give up an idea once he was sure it was right.

The first issue of the *Monthly Gospel Visitor,* printed in April 1851, was mailed to about three hundred subscribers. Today its successor, the *Gospel Messenger,* has a weekly circulation of about forty-five thousand copies.

— *Mary Garber*

On Both Sides of the Battle Lines

JOHN KLINE (1797-1864)

"I never saw John Kline leave a home," testified an aged woman, "without first taking the hand of each young person present and saying something special to him, often in a low tone. I do not know what he said to others, but he once said to me, 'Do not neglect the salvation of your soul. It is the one thing needful.' I have never forgotten it."

This happened in the days when children were supposed to be seen and not heard. And when company came, they waited until the second or third table to eat, no matter how late it got to be or how hungry they were.

This Brethren minister, who had no children of his own, was nevertheless the friend of all the young people who knew him in person and of others who may have heard about him.

"I make it a rule," said John Kline, "never to leave a home without trying to create an impression for good."

But it must have been the shining eyes of the children, who listened breathlessly, that kept him telling his wonderful stories far into the night. And what stories John Kline could tell!

"I feel as if I have been there," one child would whisper to another as they finally had to go to bed.

Some of these young people had never been far from the mountain cabins in which they were born. They saw only a few neighbors and sometimes did not get their mail for months at a time in the winter. Radio and television probably had not entered their wildest dreams; much less had space marvels. John Kline's visits were the most exciting, and sometimes the most important, happenings in their whole lives.

"Come in, come in," welcomed father, mother, and children as they ran to meet their good friend on his faithful horse, Nell.

"Thank you," answered Brother Kline. "But may I attend to the needs of my horse first? She has had a long, hard trip."

The father and the boys would go with Brother Kline to the stable with Nell while the mother and the girls hurried into the cabin to prepare the meal. No one wanted to miss a single moment with the preacher.

"I love to hear him read the Bible," said one. "God seems very near when he prays," said another. And when he spoke of the things eternal, the things that last, everyone that heard him wanted to try to live better.

Someone always asked him where he had been. John Kline had been to places which they had only heard or read about. It was thrilling to hear him tell of his ride on "train cars." He described Niagara Falls, one of God's wonders. And just imagine! He had been to Washington, D. C., the capital of the United States. He had talked to men high up in the government. He once wrote in his diary, which he kept accurately for more than twenty-nine years, "I had a pleasant visit with President Fillmore."

When John Kline was the visitor, that was one time that the children of the home did not mind getting up early. Why? Because they knew that he got up early and there was always the chance that they might have a few minutes alone with him. To watch a sunrise with him, or to hear him talk about God and His creation, was something to live by.

This Brethren minister lived on a fine farm in the beautiful Shenandoah Valley of Virginia. He could attend the Linville Creek church, which was located on one end of his farm. He had the care of this church for many years. But he knew that some Brethren families lived in places hard to get to, far from any towns, railroads, or churches. They needed preaching, too. It was the need of these people that appealed to him. He spent many weary hours climbing steep trails in all kinds of weather. He met white people and Indians who could have been friends or enemies. He risked his life crossing flooded streams. He traveled about one hundred thousand miles in his lifetime, mostly on horseback, to preach.

And how was he paid for all this? He wasn't paid in dollars and cents. He served on his own time and paid his own expenses.

When this man became interested in medicine, it was an added blessing to the people he visited. "When Brother Kline comes, I will ask him what to do for my child who is sick," a mother would say. "Perhaps he will bring some medicine."

And now the faithful horse, Nell, had some steeper places to go. Herbs and roots from the meadows and the mountains were gathered and made into medicine. "There is no charge," John Kline always said to a grateful patient who was too poor to pay anything. This great missionary, like some of our missionaries today, ministered to the people's bodies as well as to their souls.

One evening, in the fall of 1850, two Brethren preachers rode up to a farmhouse in Union County, Pennsylvania. One of these ministers was Elder John Kline. Visiting the churches in Virginia, Maryland, and Pennsylvania, they had been traveling nineteen days and had preached in many churches.

"Come in, Brother Kline," exclaimed the deacon with great surprise and joy. "We are very glad to see you."

As they sat around the large fireplace that night talking, John Kline noticed a twelve-year-old boy who sat quietly back in the corner and did not say anything. The man was all physician now. He asked the parents about the boy.

"He has been sick for five years," they told him. "There does not seem to be any hope that he will ever be well. He is very discouraged."

Then John Kline talked to the boy. He asked him many questions. He told him what medicine and herbs to get and how to take them. And he told him how to take care of himself. "If you will follow my directions," he said, "you will get well."

The sick boy went to bed that night happier than he had been for many years. The next morning, he was up early. He did not want to miss one minute with the man who had given him hope. That boy was J. G. Royer, who later as teacher, preacher, writer, and college president served the Church of the Brethren in active work for over fifty years.

When you study the history of the United States, the names of military leaders appear in the Civil War period. But when you read the history of the Church of the Brethren in the same period, the name of John Kline stands out as that of a courageous leader. Some of the worst of the fighting was near his own home.

Elder John Kline was one of those who lost his life during the Civil War. He was not a military soldier. He was a soldier of peace. He was a friend to everyone.

The Brethren had come to Virginia and other Confederate states from Pennsylvania to get away from the evils of the Revolutionary War. Since that time, many churches had been organized. The Brethren had preached and lived their beliefs about peace. They had preached against slavery. Some government officials knew some of the leaders of the Church of the Brethren personally; but others did not, and they could not or would not understand why Brethren would not fight.

These were sad days for the Brethren in the South. Like other Brethren, Brother Kline was loyal to the State of Virginia, but he did not want to see the Union broken. When war came, John Kline did everything he could to help the Brethren.

On December 16, 1861, he wrote a letter which began, "My dear friend Colonel Lewis," and ended, "From your friend, John Kline." This letter was one of the things that helped to secure the passing of the Exemption Act, which said that Brethren would not have to go into the army if they would pay a fine. This made some people — even some of John Kline's neighbors, who had always known him — very angry.

From his diary we read that he and some other Brethren were arrested. "Saturday, April 5, 1862. This forenoon I am about home. In the afternoon I am taken to Harrisonburg and put in the guard house. My place is in the large jury room in the court house, upstairs, with others who are captives with myself."

What do you suppose this Brethren minister did? He tells us in his own words: "I aim at comforting my brother captives and myself with the recollection that Paul was once a captive like ourselves and that in this state of imprisonment, he preached upon the text that I have selected today."

One dark night during this terrible war, there came a knock on John Kline's door.

"Can you come help a man?" asked the neighbor standing there.

"Yes," answered Brother Kline. "What is the trouble?"

"He has been in the Southern army, but he was trying to escape to the North where he would be safe. He is badly hurt; perhaps his leg is broken."

"Where is he now?"

"He is at my home," answered Abraham Funk. "We must keep it a secret to save his life. It will be dangerous for you to be seen. You know that people are watching you closely."

"Just wait until I get my medicines," answered John Kline.

People watched him even more when he went to Annual Conference in Indiana. He crossed into Northern territory and came back into Southern territory. Words like *spy* and *traitor* were heard. John Kline told friends, "I am threatened; they may take my life; but I do not fear them; they can only kill my body."

It was on the morning of June 15, 1864, that John Kline was riding Nell home from the blacksmith shop. As he passed a ridge of timberland, he was shot from ambush and killed. His horse went on home alone.

All of his life, John Kline had worked as if he knew he had a time limit.

"I believe," he said, "that satisfaction with one's self is the work of the Evil One. I try to improve my work and to do more work. I have a plan of life and I stick to it."

— Mary Garber

A Brave Man of Peace

PETER R. WRIGHTSMAN (1834-18??)

"Dear Father, save me from these men. Have mercy upon them and turn them from their evil course, and save Thy servant." Peter R. Wrightsman was praying while soldiers cursed and threatened him.

Had the soldiers come out to capture some dangerous criminal? Oh, no. Peter R. Wrightsman was a young Church of the Brethren minister. He lived on a farm, in Washington County, Tennessee, during the Civil War. He did not have a gun. He had not broken any laws. He had not harmed anyone. He had only tried to help people. But there was a terrible war going on and he, as a member of the Church of the Brethren, did not believe in war. Brethren wanted to live in love and peace; but some people did not understand. For this reason, many Brethren were treated unkindly and spitefully, sometimes even by their neighbors. Some lost their property. Some even lost their lives.

It was not the first time that Southern soldiers had come to the Wrightsman farm. From time to time for three years they came and took the crops, the horses, and anything else they could find. They did not pay for any of the things they took. At last, there was only one horse left. The family had hoped and prayed that they would be allowed to keep that one to use in planting their crops. But, in the summer of 1863, a squad of rough soldiers rode up to the farm to take this last horse. They were yelling and cursing.

"I believe they have come to kill me," said Peter Wrightsman to himself.

"We know you still have a horse. Where is it?" demanded the soldiers.

"Maybe this preacher's horse doesn't believe in war either," sneered a sullen-looking soldier. "Maybe he wants to stay on the farm, while others go out and fight for him."

"Part of you go to the pasture to get the horse," commanded one of the soldiers. "The others stay here with me to guard this man."

What did Peter Wrightsman do? He told about it himself, later. "I just stepped inside the stable, with my hands upward, and prayed to my heavenly Father," he said. "I never exercised stronger faith in prayer than at that time. It seemed as if I was speaking face to face with my blessed Lord."

When he came back to the soldiers, he knew God had answered his prayer. "I felt I could see the evil look going out of their faces like the shadow of a cloud before the bright sunlight," he testified.

"Mr. Wrightsman, can we get some bread?" then asked the soldiers meekly, staring at the face of the minister. They shifted uneasily in their saddles. One by one, they put their guns away. They did not know what it was, but they knew something had happened.

"Oh, yes," answered Brother Wrightsman. "We love to feed the hungry."

He went into the house and said to his sisters. "Please cut off a large slice of bread and butter it for each of the soldiers."

He took the buttered bread out into the yard and handed a slice of it to each soldier. They bowed and thanked the young man. Then they rode away, taking his last horse.

"But I felt happy," said this brave man of peace. "I felt sure the Lord had saved my life."

However, this young man's troubles were not over. He had joined the church when he was twenty-three years old. Three years later, he was elected to the ministry and served well. This was a very young age for a minister in those days, especially since he was not married yet!

War takes young men. But the church was shocked when their young minister was drafted and another member was arrested on a false charge.

"Through the power of our heavenly Father and the help of our friends," said these Brethren men, "we were saved from prison and perhaps death."

The Confederate government had agreed that members of the Church of the Brethren would not have to serve in the army if they paid a fine of five hundred dollars. But toward the last of the war, when the South needed men badly, the local authorities arrested and shut up many Brethren in prisons and stockades, even after they had paid the fine.

At a council meeting in the Limestone church, a petition was drawn up asking the government to release the Brethren from prison and military service. But who would carry the petition to Richmond? Nobody wanted to do it.

"Why not get young Peter Wrightsman to do it?" asked some of the older members.

Peter Wrightsman did not want to go either, but he said, "If you and the church will pray for me, I will go."

At one time during the long train trip Brother Wrightsman and a minister from North Carolina were the only passengers on the train who were not soldiers. When this minister found out that Wrightsman was a Brethren minister and opposed to war, he began to argue with him. While Wrightsman explained his Brethren faith, soldiers sat all around him. Some muttered threats.

Was the young minister scared? "I felt the Lord was with me," he said. "I was not the least alarmed." Continuing on his journey, he went to the Confederate Congress and made his plea. How happy he was that he could bring the petition back marked "Granted"!

In the fall of 1864, members of the Limestone church discussed having a love feast. "Everything seems quiet just now," they said. "Let us set the fourth Saturday of September for our meeting."

Everyone being happy to be able to meet again, a large crowd started for the church. But when they got within sight of the church, they saw a regiment of soldiers on the grounds.

"Let us turn back," urged many frightened members. "We must give up the idea of a service."

"No," said Peter Wrightsman. "Let us go on with the meeting. Perhaps the Lord has sent them to this place to hear the gospel."

It was a great meeting. "It was one of the best love feasts I ever attended," many people declared. "You could feel the very presence of God." The soldiers were invited in. "Couldn't you come and preach the gospel in our communities after the war?" some asked afterward.

Peter R. Wrightsman did preach the gospel in many places, after he married Elizabeth Witter and was graduated from medical school in Cincinnati, Ohio. He preached in Ohio, Indiana, Kansas, Georgia, and Texas.

— Mary Garber

The Boy With the Donkey

JAMES QUINTER (1816-1888)

"Keep steady! Keep steady, little Jackie. Nothing will hurt you."

These were the words that James Quinter said over and over into the large flopping ears of his little donkey as he and the donkey did the work assigned to them. There were reasons for Jackie to be afraid. Indeed, it was often difficult for James himself not to be. All about them were roaring fires, so hot that they melted iron ore and stone. James and Jackie had to steer around the hottest places and work their way carefully between the men who fired these furnaces or pounded the red-hot iron.

James was only eight years old. Jackie was only three. They worked in an iron foundry at Phoenixville, Pennsylvania. Jackie was hitched to a little steel cart. Their job was to go about in the foundry and pick up the iron which the men and the machines were shaping. They moved it on the cart from one man or one machine to the next until it was completed. Since there were always loud noises in the foundry, James found it easier to walk in front of Jackie and lead him than to walk behind him and shout directions. This was why the men often heard him say, "Don't be afraid, Jackie. I'll show you the way."

All through his later life, James Quinter was to be a great leader — a leader of men. Perhaps it was the lessons he and Jackie learned together which enabled him to

79

succeed. His poise and quietness of spirit seemed always to say to the people whom he was leading, "Do not be afraid. Let us proceed carefully and we will find the way."

Born in Philadelphia in 1816, James was thirteen when his father died. Since the boy seemed very eager and able to learn, his mother and his two sisters tried to make it possible for him to continue in school. He under-

took to keep a store and attend college part time, but, finding this too difficult, he moved in with a family near Ursinus College and worked to pay his way.

It was in this community, while he lived with Mr. and Mrs. Fitzwater and helped them on the farm, that James made many important decisions which affected the remainder of his life. Church of the Brethren preachers coming into this community met with the people in their homes for preaching and prayer services. James liked to attend these services.

One evening James ran from the barn to the house, calling to Mrs. Fitzwater, "I've found it! I've found it!" Mrs. Fitzwater, seeing the smile on his face and the gleam in his eye and knowing that he had found something important, asked, "What have you found?" James replied, "I've found peace with God."

Soon after this experience he was baptized. After that, although he was only seventeen years old, he would give his testimony with the others when the Brethren met in their prayer meetings. He always spoke in a kind and humble way. All the other people could see that he had indeed found peace with God and that God was as close to him as if He actually stood by his side.

When James was eighteen, he began to teach school. On Sundays and on prayer-meeting nights he helped with the church services, doing well whatever he did. Four years later the people of the congregation voted that he should become a minister and preach to them. After many hours in prayer, he decided that teaching and preaching would fit nicely together.

At this time James began a practice which he followed throughout life. He got up early in the morning, read the Bible, then knelt beside his bed to begin the day with prayer. When the day's work was done he again went to his room, read from the Bible, and closed the day with prayer. Once each month he found time to spend an entire day in fasting and prayer. Later in life, he gathered his family about him each day while he read to them from the Bible, all of them joining in prayer. From the beginning of his ministry he was known as "the praying preacher."

He might have continued in this community for most of his life. He had an income from his schoolteaching; he preached in the church; he was well liked by the people. But one day some officials of the church came to visit him. They said, "James, we believe that the church is calling you to become a missionary; to leave this community, where the church is now well established, and to journey westward to open other churches."

James replied, "But I am only a young man. There are others who could do it better."

After he had prayed about it, he felt this to be God's call to him. Joining one or two others, he made a long trip across Pennsylvania on horseback. When he returned home he took up his teaching again.

Some people in western Pennsylvania whom he had visited on this trip called him to come and help build a church among them. He felt that he should go. Taking his mother and his sisters with him, he settled on a small farm and began to establish a church. Out from this church he traveled to preach in other communities. On one such preaching trip he baptized fifty-two persons. He became known as a great evangelist. He was so busy with the work of the church that he did not marry until he was thirty-four years old.

James always liked to go to the Annual Conference. In those days traveling to and from Conference was quite an undertaking. Sometimes he would go by train, but it was often necessary to go by carriage or horseback, perhaps for several hundred miles. Since he was an educated man he was asked to become the Conference secretary and to keep the minutes of the meeting. He did this year after year, becoming well known for his ability to write well and to help the people to reach the right decisions.

In 1856, he traveled on the same train with Henry Kurtz of Ohio, who had begun publishing the *Gospel Visitor* in 1851. As they talked together about the new church magazine, James gave the best advice he could.

As a result of their friendship, Henry Kurtz asked him to move to Ohio to assist in the editing of the magazine. It was a hard decision to make. But, for a second time, James felt the call of God to move westward. Taking his family with him, he began a new life in Ohio.

James deeply loved the Church of the Brethren and his first editorial writing for the *Gospel Visitor* was concerned with the unity of the church. But he had yet another interest for the church which he now began to emphasize. He believed that education should be more common among the Brethren and that the church should have a college of its own.

James, who had by this time become known everywhere as Brother Quinter, felt that God was calling him to start a college. Trying to establish this first college, he had to think of securing classrooms, a library, teachers, textbooks, and places for the students to live and eat. The costs for attending this school were very low in comparison with costs today. Then the fourteen-week term cost about forty-five dollars; today the twelve-week term costs about four hundred dollars.

But almost at the same time the college was started, the Civil War began. The school had to close. When the war was over, another school was started at Huntingdon, Pennsylvania, and Brother Quinter was invited to become its president; it later became Juniata College. While serving as the president of this school, he continued to write editorials for the church paper, which, having been combined with some other papers, was now called the *Gospel Messenger*.

In addition to being widely known as a preacher, a church leader and editor, and a schoolteacher and college president, James Quinter did other things which also made him well known. He became a religious debater. He would meet with ministers of other church groups and debate doctrines and practices such as baptism; sometimes great crowds of people came together to hear these men debate. Brother Quinter always presented his arguments calmly, clearly, and in love. This made him popular as a debater. In addition, he became interested in hymns and songs, believing that the great doctrines of the church could be taught through them. He published many hymns and edited a book about those being used at that time in the churches.

In 1888, when Brother Quinter was seventy-three years old, he went to the Annual Conference at North Manchester, Indiana. The large congregation was pleased when he was called upon to lead in the closing prayer. The Church of the Brethren was divided on some matters of policy at that time, and many of the members were feeling uncertain and confused. But as Brother Quinter went forward, looking dignified and kindly, the congregation seemed to feel as if he were saying the same words he had often said to Jackie in the foundry: "Do not be afraid. We will find the way."

As he knelt to pray, all listened closely or prayed with him. Just as he said, "O God, we thank Thee that we have met . . . ," his voice suddenly was stilled.

Thus came to an end a noble life. In boyhood he had been surrounded by noisy machines and dangerous foundry equipment; through all this he had led Jackie. In his later years, through troubled and confusing times, he had led his people with patience and kindliness, as God gave him wisdom. Under his wise leadership, many found the way of life.

— *Desmond W. Bittinger*

From Slavery to the Ministry

SAMUEL WEIR (1812-1884)

A little girl, ten years old, taught a thirty-year-old man to read. And that was not all. Catherine Long, the little girl, was white and the man was black! But that did not matter to them. The man read his Bible through many times and learned its teachings so well that he gave helpful talks to his people and he was sometimes asked to speak to white people.

On one occasion it was announced, five weeks ahead of time, that a former Negro slave would speak at the Bush meetinghouse in Southern Ohio. A large crowd was present. The speaker used as his text Hebrews 11: 1-2. At the end of the message, everyone voted to call Samuel Weir to the ministry. Not one person voted against it. And on that day in August 1849, the first Negro was installed into the ministry of the Church of the Brethren.

He was born a slave in Bath County, Virginia, on April 15, 1812. We know nothing of his parents. What did being a slave mean? For one thing, it meant that a person could be bought and sold, whenever his owner wished, just like a cow or a horse.

One day, when Samuel was twelve years old, his owner, William Byrd, said to him, "Sam, get your things together. Your new master will soon be here to get you. I have sold you to Mr. Andrew McClure."

The boy looked up frightened, "Oh, Master Byrd,"

he began while big tears filled his eyes and rolled down his cheeks.

"Here, here, none of that," said the slave owner. "You must be a good worker for Mr. McClure. He paid me two hundred eighty dollars for you. You will like it fine with him if you work hard and behave yourself."

"Yes, master," answered the heartbroken boy, choking back the sobs. He looked around. This was the only home he had ever known. The other Negro slaves were the only friends he had ever known. Now he had to leave everyone — his friends and perhaps his mother and brothers and sisters. He felt as if he just couldn't do it. But, being a slave, he had to do it. He could not say what he wanted to do. His life was not his own!

But he must have been a good worker and he must have done what was right because he served Mr. McClure until he was thirty years old. Then something happened that made him realize that all the terrible things did not happen to slaves; the white people could suffer, too.

The news of the tragedy spread fast. "The McClures' little son was killed," neighbors told each other.

"How did it happen?" was the question. No one knew exactly, except that he was thrown from a horse.

Samuel Weir was sad, too. He loved the little boy. He couldn't bear to look at the sad faces of his master and mistress.

"I wish I could do something to help," he sighed.

"We cannot go on like this," said the father of the little boy. "We must get help somewhere."

"The members of the Church of the Brethren have been very kind," said the mother. "I would like to go there. Perhaps if we joined that church we could find help."

Elder Peter Nead was the minister at that time. He

spoke kindly to the sorrowing parents. "The Church of the Brethren is opposed to slavery. We believe it is not following the teachings of Jesus to own a slave. We do not receive slave owners into our fellowship. Would you like to read some of the scriptures on which we base our beliefs?"

It was not long before the McClures came to Peter Nead and said, "We have made Samuel Weir a free man. We believe the Church of the Brethren is right in teaching that slavery is not following the teaching of Jesus. We want to be baptized."

That really surprised some of the people. "I simply do not understand the McClures," said one. "They were offered fifteen hundred dollars for Sam Weir, by slave traders."

Samuel Weir did not understand either. He just could not believe it. "I must find out about this wonderful change in my master," he declared. He talked with the minister and later he, too, was baptized by Peter Nead on May 14, 1843.

But members of the Church of the Brethren were uneasy. "You know the laws of Virginia are that though a slave has been made free, if he stays in the state over a year after being set free he can be sold again. What will Samuel Weir do?" they asked each other.

"I will go to the free state of Ohio," said he.

"And I will give you what you need for the trip," said the kind white man who had been his master. "You are my brother in Christ now."

"Elder B. F. Moomaw in Botetourt County will be able to advise us. He has relatives in Twin Valley, Ohio," said Peter Nead. "Perhaps he would go with you. You would be safe with him. He is well-known and respected by men high in government."

It was a long journey. No doubt many people thought Elder Moomaw and Samuel Weir made a strange pair. But the two Brethren men did not think so. After they crossed the Ohio River, the first stop they made was at the home of Thomas and Sarah Major. And from there they came to the home of John Moomaw in Twin Valley.

On Sunday, November 5, 1843, B. F. Moomaw told the story of the former slave to the Paint Creek Church of the Brethren. "We will receive this colored brother into our membership," they said after listening carefully to the story.

"Come, make my home your home," invited William Bryant, a minister of the church. So this man, who was born a slave, found a happy home. Here he learned to read, taught by Catherine Long, the minister's little granddaughter.

He not only learned to read the Bible, but he lived its teachings. Soon he was asked to speak.

After he was called to the ministry, he was told, "Now you go to members of your own race and hold meetings to help them." This appealed to him as the right thing to do. For sixteen years he lived among the Negro people, preaching, teaching, and helping in other ways. What a long time to wait! But finally two colored people said they were ready to be baptized. How happy the minister was!

A thousand people came to this baptism! This was the beginning of the Frankfort church. Samuel Weir served here and among the colored people at other places in the Scioto Valley for thirty-two years.

Samuel Weir did not preach what the Bible said and then go out and live differently himself. He lived what he preached. And he made many friends, among both white and colored people. One white minister was an especially good friend. Brother Weir told him about a great wish of his heart.

"I would like to leave my house and lot as a gift for a church for my colored brethren," he said. "I hope that God will let me live long enough to pay off the mortgage, so that I can give it to them."

"Do not worry about that," said William D. Mallow in his kind way. "I will take care of your debt."

"Thank God!" said this good man. "Now I can die in peace."

Samuel Weir loved the Church of the Brethren. He worked for the church. He read the Bible and he tried to live as Jesus lived, helping everyone who needed it. He was a friend to both white and black people. When he died, some people said of him, "He was the best man in Frankfort."

— Mary Garber

In Search of a Church

CHRISTIAN HOPE (1844-1899)

Nobody would have expected him — this small, mild-mannered man, whose broken speech was very difficult for Americans to understand — to be the one to stir the conscience of a whole denomination. But people noticed that when Christian Hope began to talk about his Lord his face became radiant and his whole being was transformed. They noticed, and they remembered.

It took him many years of earnest searching to find the Church of the Brethren, then known as the German Baptist Brethren, but only one year to challenge them into sending him abroad as their first foreign missionary.

He was born in Denmark in 1844. "We will make of this boy a preacher," his father said; but the mother would not hear of this for her son. However, there was agreement between them that the lad should have an education. In fact, the family deprived itself of everything but the barest necessities that the only son might go to school. Later he learned the trade of harnessmaker.

Christian early became dissatisfied with the state church and in 1865 was baptized by the Baptists in the North Sea. Choosing the ministry, he began preaching vigorously and constantly; during one four-month period he preached three hundred forty sermons. He held that the Bible is the Word of God and can be understood by the common man. He preached and wrote against the prevailing military system; this brought him to prison, but the court let him off with a light sentence. Hope promptly resumed his preaching and it soon became necessary for him to leave Denmark in a hurry to avoid arrest. Emigrating to the United States, he settled for a time in central Iowa, where he married Mary Nielsen. Later he moved to Clinton, Iowa, where he united with the American Baptists and preached for the Swedish Baptists in Rock Island, Illinois.

But in spite of his activities he was still not satisfied; he wanted to find a church which would more nearly meet his convictions. One day, in the back of a family Bible, he happened onto a short sketch about the Church of the Brethren. Its principles appealed to him. Here was a church, he felt, which practiced what the Bible teaches. From that day forward he searched for the Brethren — in Chicago, in New York, and in Philadelphia — but nowhere could he find them.

He did not give up his search. And at last, in 1874, somebody told him, "If you'll go over into Illinois, near Mount Carroll, you'll find a Brethren church." This was wonderful news. Hope immediately closed his harness shop and with his father-in-law set out on foot for Carroll County, Illinois.

It was harvesttime in northern Illinois, and a scorcher of a day, when the two men came to the home of George D. Zollers. That night he had his talk with Zollers and learned that his host preached regularly at the nearby Hickory Grove church. On Sunday morning Zollers took the visitors to the meeting.

We should not overlook George Zollers, the man who preached the first Brethren sermon that Hope had ever heard. Zollers was born in Montgomery County, Pennsylvania, in 1841, into a large and poor family. He secured an education somehow and learned the plastering trade. He spent some years in a whaling expedition and at the age of twenty-five went west to Carroll County, where he followed his trade. When the Hickory Grove congregation called him to the ministry he was reluctant to accept, because he felt unprepared for the work. After much prayer and counseling, he finally agreed to accept the call. For twenty-eight years he served the church. It has been said of him that he had a deep secret prayer life which spilled over into his sermons; it never angered his hearers, but melted the hearts of many. During the winters, when the farm work was light and folks did not want any plastering done, Zollers held revival meetings. He baptized Christian Hope on October 25, 1874.

Hope settled in Mount Carroll but later moved to nearby Lanark, where his friends helped set him up in the harnessmaking business. Meanwhile, he was writing enthusiastic letters to his friends in Denmark, telling of his joy in finding the Brethren. He also sent them tracts, written by Brethren J. H. Moore and M. M. Eshelman, which he had translated into the Danish language. His Danish friend, Christian Hansen, greatly impressed by the tracts and the letters, wrote asking for baptism.

The Brethren of the Northern Illinois District were faced with a momentous decision: Should they send someone to Denmark to baptize this man? Some opposed it, but others saw in his request a similarity to Paul's Macedonian call and said to each other, "Is not this also a call from God, to go over into Denmark and help them?" A special district meeting was called to meet at the Cherry Grove church on November 12, 1875. After much prayer and serious discussion, the members present decided to send a representative of the church to Denmark. They elected Hope to the ministry and chose him to go to

Denmark, with two other brethren. The district also put notices in Brethren periodicals, asking for funds to help them with the Danish mission.

The new missionary promptly sold his harness business and with his wife and child sailed for Denmark, arriving in February 1876. Since the brethren chosen to go with him could not make the trip until later, the Hopes had to go alone.

Hope could not find good housing for his family, and he had little money, for many of the Brethren back home were not convinced that he should be paid a salary. This meant real hardship for Hope and his wife.

Hope tried earnestly not to be a burden on the churches at home. He slept on the floor, in barns, and sometimes even in fields, and spent not a cent for a warm meal. Walking as much as possible, he traveled constantly. While he preached daily, he still found time to prepare tracts and even wrote a little paper which he circulated among the people.

On May 5, 1876, he had the deep satisfaction of baptizing Christian Hansen — the first member of the Church of the Brethren to be baptized in Europe since the church emigrated from Germany early in the eighteenth century.

On October 29 Enoch Eby and Daniel Fry and their wives arrived in Brondeslev, Denmark, and found ten members waiting. Soon three more were baptized and a love feast was held. Hope was ordained to the eldership and C. Eskildsen was called to the ministry. The Ebys and the Frys remained until March 1878, when they returned to America.

Hope continued his work; in 1885 he went into Sweden, preached there, and started a little Sunday school. He discovered considerable antagonism from the state church, but his work and that of others stirred up the church, causing it to start Sunday schools of its own and to become active in young people's work and in evangelism.

In 1886 Mary Hope became ill and Hope himself was not well; so they regretfully returned to America. Three times Brother Hope went back to Denmark, traveling widely, preaching a few sermons here and there, then going on to other communities.

His mission to Denmark had been opposed by some, and his direct methods were sometimes misunderstood. But, as a whole, the church in America appreciated him and felt that he deserved more compensation than he had received. The people took up offerings and purchased a house for him in Kansas. This gift was gratefully received by Hope, and his financial burden became less oppressive. But it was not in him to be idle about the Lord's work. He began preaching among the Danes and the Swedes in Kansas and Nebraska, among whom he soon had considerable influence.

The Danish mission was closed eventually and some have said that it was a failure; but through it Christian Hope blazed the trail for foreign missions in the Church of the Brethren.

The church owes much to this humble man of small means, this earnest seeker for truth, this dedicated preacher whose sense of mission touched the hearts of the Brethren and led them to find new meaning in Christ's injunction, "Go ye therefore, and teach all nations."

— *Ota Lee Russell*

With Face Turned Toward India

WILBUR B. STOVER (1866-1930)

A world-famous doctor, Charles Mayo, one time gave some rules for success in life: (1) Choose what you like to do. (2) Stick to it. (3) Keep cheerful.

That could be a thumbnail sketch of the life of Wilbur Brenner Stover, the first missionary of the Church of the Brethren to a non-Christian land. He always wanted to be a minister or a missionary. He literally "sold" the Church of the Brethren on missions. He kept on until he turned the church from *little* discussions to a *big* task.

Like Hannah in the Bible story, Wilbur Stover's mother dedicated him to the Lord before he was born. Having lost a son, she promised God to give Wilbur for His work. And Wilbur never thought of anything else.

The father of this pioneer missionary to India must also have had some pioneer spirit. During the rush to the West, Jacob A. Stover went as far as Pike's Peak. However, he came back east and started to teach school. After a time he married one of his pupils, Mollie C. Lasher.

But they did not "live happily ever after" as in a fairy tale. This was real life. The young husband enlisted in the infantry during the Civil War. It was while he was away that their son, Edgar, died.

"We need God's help," said the father when he came home. "I have seen all of war that I ever want to see.

Our son is gone. Life is uncertain for all of us. Let's give our lives to God."

The young parents joined the Church of the Brethren. Soon Jacob Stover was called to the ministry. The years that followed were busy and happy ones. On a farm near Greencastle, Pennsylvania, Wilbur Stover and his three brothers were born. His father farmed and started a nursery. He taught school in winter and he also conducted singing schools.

But one day while he was grafting, his knife slipped and he cut his thumb. He went at once to the doctor — but this was before the day of the wonder drugs. In a few days he was dead of lockjaw.

"How will Mollie ever manage with those four little boys?" said neighbors and friends.

"I will help my mother," declared Wilbur, the oldest, doing his nine-year-old best to comfort her.

He did his best, too, to help earn money. While yet a boy, he went to work on a dairy farm. Guess what he earned. Four dollars a month! But it helped. At the same time he went to school, walking nearly two miles twice a day; nor were there many absent or tardy marks against his name. Later, he worked in a store in Hagerstown, Maryland. "It was good experience," said Wilbur when he was older. "I learned how to meet people, how to take care of my money, something about business, and how to work."

While he worked, this thought was always in his mind: "Someday I am going to be a minister or a missionary." It was like a refrain.

One day, when Wilbur was just a little boy, some men came to his mother's house asking for money to build the Shady Grove church. "I want to help, too," he said; and he gave fifty cents from his small savings. "Here is where I made my first contribution for a house of God," he would often say in later years.

It was easy for Wilbur Stover to talk about God, the Bible, and the church because his religion was part of his life.

But life was never easy for Wilbur. When his family lived at Warrenville, Illinois, he worked on a farm and in a gristmill. It could not be easy for a big, strong man to lift heavy sacks of wheat and flour, and surely it was harder still for a young man with a small frame. But there was Wilbur Stover doing it when one day President J. G. Royer of Mount Morris College saw him and invited him to attend the college and study the business course to learn to keep books.

"You may have free tuition because you are a minister's son," promised President Royer.

In the fall of 1884, W. B. Stover entered Mount Morris College to learn bookkeeping. But he learned something else also; he learned that he wanted more education.

"I will choose the classical course," said he, "because here I will study some of the world's best literature."

But most important of all, following a series of evangelistic meetings at the college, he was baptized into the Church of the Brethren on March 8, 1885. What a great day that was for the Church of the Brethren!

The first thing he did was to write a letter to his mother, telling her about the meetings, his conversion, and the great joy in his heart. "This marks a change in my life," he wrote. "From now on, my life and my work shall be for Christ and His church."

Wilbur Stover was what we call an "all out" person. He never did anything by halves. It was all or nothing with him. "He just bubbles over with energy and the joy of living," said his friends. "It's always pleasant to be with Wilbur, even if one can't go along with all his schemes. He is always doing something. Nobody could be bored around him."

Now he transferred all this energy to the church. "I believe every Christian should be an active worker in the church," he declared. "There is work for everybody. Everybody should be working."

"How do you like being in charge of the primary department in Sunday school?" asked his fellow students.

"Fine, just fine," he answered. "It is the place to begin to teach missions."

Two words in the last verse of the last chapter of the Gospel of Matthew stood out in his mind. These words were *go* and *teach*.

Now, W. B. Stover's whole mind and being was filled with the idea of missions. He studied about missions. He talked about missions in his room, on the campus, or anywhere else anyone would listen. He wrote about missions. "Could your essay be about missions?" sometimes the students would tease. But Wilbur Stover only nodded and smiled happily.

When he was reminded that the Church of the Brethren had no mission in non-Christian lands, he said, "I know, but it is my business to get the church ready."

In the meantime, he kept on going to school to get himself ready. But it cost money to go to college then as it does today. The only way he could see was to drop out of school for a year to earn money to continue. But how should he try to earn it? One of his teachers had told him, "I worked my way through college by selling pictures for homes. But it is hard work and there are many problems."

Hard work never scared Wilbur Stover. "It sounds

good to me," he said. So he signed up. The next year he was back in Mount Morris with a thousand dollars and some rules of his own for good salesmanship.

1. Talk up your goods. Never run down another's business.
2. Make no appeal to try to arouse sympathy for yourself.
3. Concentrate on business.
4. Remember your mother; write to her.
5. Read good books.
6. Keep active in church work.
7. Don't forget to pray.

Wilbur Stover liked to trace kinship between people. He was always telling students about some unknown relative of theirs. Sometimes it was interesting to them. Sometimes it wasn't.

But it was very interesting to the man, himself, to discover that he was related to a certain girl at Mount Morris College. She was Mary Emmert. So it was "Cousin Mary" and "Cousin Wilbur." But not for long. The kinship ran pretty far back anyway. Soon they fell in love. On June 29, 1893, they were married. It was an until-death-do-thee-part marriage. In India or in America, the Stovers' five children always had a beautiful home life.

They were waiting in the States until they could return to India, when God suddenly called Brother Stover home, on October 31, 1930.

There had been years of preaching, planning, writing, praying, and waiting to go to India. It all took a long time. It took much waiting — but Wilbur Stover believed in waiting. It took much patience — but he had a great deal of it. It took much faith in both God and man — and he had that also. He believed in working too; so he worked while he waited.

The years that have followed have shown that all this was well worth while. Little by little the church changed and began to believe what he wrote in his book, *The Great First-Work of the Church,* that spreading the gospel in all the world is truly the great first-work given to the church. At last the church was willing to send its first missionaries to a non-Christian country. A total of one hundred forty missionaries have been sent to that land by the Brethren in these years; and in addition many have been sent to China, Nigeria, and Ecuador.

And then there were the wonderful years in which the Stovers were working at the big task of beginning the Church of the Brethren mission in India. They spent twenty-seven years in this work. During those years they did many different kinds of work: preaching to both non-Christians and Christians; teaching the Indian people who became Christians; helping the people in times of plague and famine; taking care of orphaned children; fighting against poverty among the Indians; organizing and directing the new church. From the beginnings made at Bulsar by the Stovers and their missionary associates has come a church now numbering about nine thousand members, with strong leaders among the Indian Christians.

If Wilbur Stover could see today all these results of his efforts, he would say that they had all been very much worth while.

— *Mary Garber*

Bringing the World to the Brethren

D. L. MILLER (1841-1921)

It was a beautiful October day at Miller's Mill in 1841. The sparkling waters of the little Maryland creek rippled brightly between willow-lined banks as it sang its way to the Conococheague. Now and then a flaming leaf dropped into the current and was carried downstream to drift out onto the quiet, shining surface of the mill-pond. A thin sheet of water spilled over the dam, but the millrace ran full. The tumbling waters caught and turned the big wheel and splashed noisily into the channel below.

Inside the mill, great two-ton millstones, turned by the power of the stream, were slowly and steadily crushing wheat into flour — flour that would become bread to feed the Brethren families settled in the Hagerstown area.

Suddenly, from the little room below the mill where the Abram Miller family lived, came the sharp, thin wail of a new-born baby.

"Here is your son, Catherine," Elizabeth Long said with a smile as she placed the small bundle into the arms of the wife of the miller, her daughter. Catherine Miller closed her eyes as she held her firstborn close. What thoughts surged through the mind of this fine young woman? Could she guess that this tiny baby would grow up to be a great, good man, a beloved leader in the Church of the Brethren?

The new mother opened her eyes to find Abram, her young husband, smiling into them, bright with pride and joy at this wonderful event. "Our firstborn son, Abram," she whispered. "Let us call him Daniel Long, after my father."

Before little Daniel was two years old, the prospering miller moved his family across the road to a new brick house. They needed more room, for little Martin soon made his appearance, followed by Frank, Andrew, William, David, and George; several others died in infancy. At last the family was delighted by the appearance of a baby sister, Anna. The boys learned to work like their industrious father. Their mother was a thrifty housekeeper and a devoted mother, greatly loved by her children and the whole community.

Daniel was his father's chief helper at the mill. "Oh, Pap, come," he would call. Then his father would hurry in from another task to shift the heavy barrels. Daniel also learned to operate the millrace gate.

Daniel knew how to read before he started to school at the age of five. He could not remember when he learned his letters. Advancing rapidly, he was at the head of the "big class" in spelling by the time he was nine. He loved to read and would carry books with him to the fields to read at lunch and rest periods. When he tended the mill, he would read while the barrels were being filled with flour.

The terms at the little log schoolhouse lasted only four months during the winter. Daniel attended until he was twelve; then he began to work full time, having only two more school terms before he was grown. This was the formal schooling of a man who was to become a college president and trustee, a preacher, a publisher, an author of books, and an editor of the church paper. He never stopped studying. As president of Mount Morris College he attended classes with the students. When he was first making plans to visit Europe and the Holy Land he spent many weeks studying the German language. He built up a personal library of thousands of volumes.

When Daniel was twelve, God called to him one night in his attic bedroom, and he answered Him with his whole

heart. However, since only grown people were accepted as church members in those days, he told no one of this experience until many years later. He was baptized when he was twenty-one.

Early in life he developed a desire to travel. In his later years he became the greatest traveler among the Brethren. Sometimes alone, sometimes with Mrs. Miller, sometimes with others of the Brethren, he made many trips to Europe, the Holy Land, India, China, Japan, Australia, and many other places little known to the

Brethren. What he saw and experienced on these trips was shared with the church through sermons, articles in the church periodicals, lectures, letters, and books. In this way he did much to turn the attention of the church to the world outside his own land. It was rightfully said of him by Galen B. Royer that "his writings did much to unify the church and raise her ideals." Truly, he brought the world to the Brotherhood.

Especially popular were his lantern-slide pictures of places he had visited, for he had early invested in one of the new-fangled stereopticans; however, at first some church officials thought it would not be right to show these pictures in the churches! It was a case of standing room only when D. L. Miller came to a church to show his pictures. The crowds came in wagons, in buggies, and on foot for miles around. They stood along the aisles and in the back of the church. In at least one instance the floor settled dangerously from the weight of the people.

But of much greater weight was the evidence that his messages were helping people in many ways. "You have done more . . . toward turning me from sin. . . ." "You have done my soul good." "That sermon ought to be printed and circulated . . . for the good it will do." "Never has my heart been so moved." Young people, especially, were affected by this pioneer experience in "visual education" that had far-reaching and lasting effect in broadening Brethren thinking about the role of the church in the world.

The long and highly useful life of D. L. Miller came to an end at Huntingdon, Pennsylvania, just at Annual Conference time in 1921.

— Frances Holsopple Fenner

A Friend of Brethren Ministers

JAMES R. GISH (1826-1896)

Once there was a man who bought and sold farms. You ask what is unusual about that? It is this: He sold them only to Brethren ministers. Yes, he really did. Why was that? Perhaps it was because he was a Brethren minister himself, and a missionary as well, who wanted the Church of the Brethren to grow.

Selling farms to Brethren ministers at cost, and on easy terms, was part of the plan of James and Barbara Gish to spread the gospel of Jesus Christ.

After the Revolutionary War, when the Brethren moved southward and westward, often two or three Brethren families would settle in the same community. Soon they would call for someone to come and preach to them. James R. Gish belonged to that group of unselfish ministers who carried the gospel to people in out-of-the-way places and who made their own living besides.

When a call to preach came, the Gishes rode horseback or muleback, or walked, to carry the gospel to needy places. James did the preaching. Aunt Barbara led the singing. Side by side they worked together for the Lord. They were real evangelists.

"This community needs a minister to live here," often they were told. From these calls the Gishes got their idea for bringing ministers to the communities. They would stay in a community until a minister was settled

105

there. Sometimes they would spend a whole summer or a whole winter helping in one place this way. They were real missionaries.

James Rufus Gish was born on a farm in Roanoke County, Virginia. But it certainly wasn't like the farms some members of the same Gish family own in the same county today! What do you think the missionary-preacher would say if he could see the big machines doing the work of many men? Perhaps he would say, "I'm glad the boys do not have to work as hard as I did on the farm. But it was fun, too. I learned a great deal about soils and crops and farms that helped me in my work in later years."

There was little money in the Gish home. "Money was always scarce in my boyhood," said James R. Gish. Sometimes the crops failed no matter how hard everyone worked. There simply was no money to buy sugar, flour, seasonings, or medicines.

"I do not mind the hard work," young James Rufus would say. And he really didn't. "And I do not mind not having money to buy some things. But, oh, how I hope I can have enough to go to school!"

But many times his father had to say, "Children, we do not have money to buy clothes and books; so you cannot go to school this year."

What do you suppose this boy did? Frown and blame his parents? Or whine that the world was against him? He did not.

"I will study the best book," he decided. "I will make the Bible my textbook."

So well did James study the Bible that he became a good preacher. He knew his Bible well. He preached in twenty-two different states. People liked to hear him preach. He helped many people. So hard did he try to live by the Bible that his life gave power to his preaching and his missionary work. On the marble block at his grave in Roanoke, Illinois, there is chiseled an open Bible with these words, "Blessed are they that do His Commandments." This sums up quite well the lives of both James and Barbara Gish.

James and Barbara were married in Virginia in 1848. James was twenty-two. Perhaps because they heard that land was cheap, they decided to go west. They bought a wagon or buckboard and drove to Woodford County, Illinois. Could you guess how long it took them? Six weeks! That was a long honeymoon trip, wasn't it?

When they got there, there were no comfortable homes or good farms waiting for them, either. There was only the vast wild prairie. They found cheap land and bought one hundred sixty acres, where the town of Roanoke now stands. The price was $1.25 an acre.

"We will build us a home," they said, "and start farming." "Home" was only a shanty, sixteen feet square and unplastered. But it was home.

There were five members of the Church of the Brethren in the new community. "Let us ask for ministers to come to hold services," they said. In 1852, the first Brethren service was held and the Gishes and six others were baptized. Four months later, James Gish was called to the ministry. He was then twenty-six years old.

After a short term of service in his home congregation, he and his wife went into the evangelistic and missionary work that was to become their lifework.

They were a wonderful Christian team. They went where they were needed. No community was too small. No place was too far away. They went where they were called. A short time before the Civil War, they held a meeting in Cedar County, Missouri, which was then more than one hundred miles from any railroad.

Do you sometimes wonder what pioneer life was really like? This we must remember: Not all of it was like the "gun-totin'" Westerns that boys and girls see today. There were God-fearing people who lived quietly. There were homes and farms and schools. There were churches. And James and Barbara Gish helped start some of these churches.

With James Gish, the Bible, and especially the New Testament, was the one book for everybody. He kept New Testaments on hand and gave them to people who had none. At one time he used some of his money to print and place on the market a pocket-size New Testament with references and marginal readings at the close of each verse.

When Brother Gish was seventy years old, he became sick. He knew he could not live; so he made a will leaving all he had to his wife. The estate was valued at about sixty thousand dollars.

"Aunt Barbara" wanted to make the right use of this money. "I do not need it all," she said. "I am eager that what I do not need will be a blessing to others."

She decided that one fifth of the money was to be used to help care for aged and needy ministers and missionaries. The remainder of it was turned over to the church to help ministers buy books at low cost. Even today, many years later, through the Gish Fund this money is helping the ministers of the Church of the Brethren to secure the books they need to make their ministry the most helpful.

— *Mary Garber*

One Whose Life Was a Sermon

JACOB D. YODER (1847-1939)

How can one have fun and be happy? Jacob D. Yoder knew the answer to that question. You can look at his life and see it.

No one around McPherson, Kansas, enjoyed life more than he did. Why? For one reason, he was always giving away his money to help other people.

"That man doesn't know how much fun he is missing by keeping his money," said Brother Yoder one day about a wealthy neighbor who held on to most of his money for his own use.

Money talks. "What!" you say. It does not really talk, of course, but the way we get it and spend it tells people, more plainly than any words could do, what things we think are most important.

"We love the church," said the Yoders with their money when they helped to build the Monitor Church of the Brethren and also the McPherson church. "We think everyone's children should have a chance to go to school," they said as they worked and gave money to build up the public schools in McPherson County. "Higher education is important to help the Church of the Brethren grow," said J. D. Yoder's money. He helped build McPherson College and sent his six children there to school.

Oh, yes! Money really talks. It talks loudly. And it makes people happy, too, if they use it as the Yoders did.

Perhaps the chief source of joy to Brother Yoder was his great interest in missions. He read many times Jesus' words, "Go ye into all the world, and preach the gospel to every creature." He enjoyed sermons on missions; and he was ready to do something about them. He liked to read about the Church of the Brethren's missions in India and China. He saw that the church needed people to take the gospel — and money to send them.

"I know what I will do," he decided. "I will adopt a missionary to support." He began paying the expenses of Myrtle F. Pollock in China, and continued for seventeen years. He had so much joy spending his money that way that he decided to support Lulu Ullom Coffman, too. Now he was supporting two missionaries in the same field. Besides that, he gave much of his land to the General Mission Board.

Jacob D. Yoder was born in Somerset County, Pennsylvania. He was the son of David C. and Susan Miller Yoder. One day David came in from working on his farm in Pennsylvania and said to his wife, "Sarah, sometimes I think I would like to buy a farm in Kansas and move there. I have heard a great deal about the rich land that is to be had there, and the wonderful crops that can be grown."

"But it is so very far away," answered his wife. "How would we ever get there with these little children? We wouldn't know anyone. And where would we go to church?"

"I would find out all of these things before we made the move. But it seems to me there is a great opportunity for people in the West. We are young. I am just thirty-two. Perhaps God could use us in His work in the new West."

The Yoders were the first members of the Church of

110

the Brethren to settle in McPherson County, Kansas. They brought their church letters from the Pike church and put them in the Peabody congregation in Harvey County, which was about fifty miles from their new home. Later the Monitor church was established near their home.

J. D. Yoder was a good farmer. He loved farming and he knew how to farm. So it was not long before he owned many acres of the rich Kansas land about which he had heard.

If you had been traveling in McPherson County in those days, perhaps you would have stayed at the Yoder home. It was only a short distance from the schoolhouse where the first church services were held. Everyone liked to go there. Everyone was welcome.

Jacob Yoder's was a large and busy household. He had six children of his own. Besides that, he hired many men and women to help with the work in the house and on the large farms. It was a happy place. It was a busy place. There was much work to do, especially at certain times. But they always had family worship. It was the rule. Nothing was allowed to interfere.

"Likewise," said one of the sons, J. J. Yoder, "on Sunday morning attending church services was a well-known duty of all. No one questioned the habit — except in time of sickness."

Jacob D. Yoder's religion was not just a Sunday religion. He lived the parable of the good Samaritan. His son said of him, "He was helpful to his neighbors, always eager to help in time of need or trouble."

He was a layman, but his life was a sermon.

— *Mary Garber*

A Trail Blazer in China

Frank H. Crumpacker (1876-1951)

"You are dumb! You will never learn the Chinese language!" A language teacher was scolding a Brethren missionary. "You had just as well go back to the United States!"

Frank Crumpacker was that missionary. But he did not go back to the United States. He had spent years preparing himself and had traveled thousands of miles to carry the message of Jesus and His love to China. Instead of going back, he and his wife with three other college mates stayed on in China to establish a Brethren mission. And for thirty years this same pioneer missionary preached and talked to the people of China in their own language.

Many years later, when Frank Crumpacker wrote about the incident with the language teacher, he said, "I cried a little. But when I left the room I mumbled, 'I will show that old teacher I can get the language.' It was a long, hard pull, but I got it."

Doing hard things was not new to Frank Crumpacker. He was born on a farm at Leeton, Missouri, May 13, 1876. During the Civil War his parents had gone from Virginia to Kansas and later to Missouri. Frank was the sixth in that family. "I learned early to take my part," said he. "I had to. Work on the farm was plentiful, and every boy had his part to do. There was plenty of play, too, but it was not ready-made and handed out as it is now."

Life must have been like a three-ringed circus on the Crumpacker farm with those eight boys. "I learned to ride young calves and mules and horses before they were tamed," said Frank. "We learned to wrestle and box. And sometimes we went further than that."

No matter what else they might want to do, the boys knew that they had to do their chores. "When I was nine years old," related Frank, "I learned to milk. At ten, I took a regular number of cows to milk morning and evening. And there were no questions about it, either."

But there was a time when the boys were late milking. It was during wheat and oats threshing time. Everyone had worked as hard as he could until late at night. The boys were so tired that they nearly fell into bed, forgetting the chores that must be done. But soon the cows let it be known that they had been forgotten. And Father Crumpacker heard them.

"Did you milk tonight?" were the terrible words that dragged the tired boys back from dreamland.

"No, sir," they answered.

"Well, the milking must be done."

Each boy who had a milking chore got up and stumbled to the barn. When they had finished, they went back to bed, half asleep when they got there. They never again forgot to do the milking.

There was no doubt about it — farm work came first on that Missouri farm. School could wait, and did.

"I had to stay by the farm work with my brothers each year until about November," said Frank. "Then we went to school until April. We walked a mile each way daily. Instead of graduating, we just kept going to school in the winter months until we had to drop out and take a man's place on the farm the year around."

Sometimes one decision a person makes changes his

113

whole life. It did for Frank Crumpacker. God's Spirit must have whispered to him. He listened. He began to feel that God had something special for him to do. He did not know yet what it was, but he knew he wanted more than a grade-school education in order to be able to do it.

When he was twenty years old, he decided to get his high school education. Since there was no high school near his home, he had to go to Fort Scott, Kansas. This schoolwork, too, had to be done little by little, as the young man had to earn his living as well as go to school. But finally he completed enough work to get a certificate to teach school.

"I got $25.00 a month and plenty of experience." Frank could laugh about it years later, but at the time it was not one bit funny. "I had to do a little work on the side to keep from going into debt. I taught a vocal music class in a church four miles away, and worked in a store on Saturdays. It was the music class that was the worst. I had to go four miles twice a week over muddy roads at night, and pass a graveyard besides."

Then he got work in a grocery store. "I must get ready to do something with my life," he declared. Was this what God wanted him to do? Would you have thought so?

"The man who owned the store was a Brethren preacher," said Cousin Frank, sharing his own faith in a letter to the writer in 1948. "I kept the store while the boss went to a council meeting in the old Paint Creek church one Saturday in June. About noon, the church people came home. The first news that came to my ears was this, 'You have been elected to become a preacher.'"

Between Sunday school and church the next day, Frank was installed into the ministry. What do you suppose were the first words he heard after being installed?

"Now you will never learn to preach any younger," said the elder-in-charge, "so take the pulpit."

"June 1948 marks my fifty years in the ministry," declared Frank. "It has been a great joy.

"But from the very beginning," Frank said, "I felt I must prepare for the ministry. I must get more education. I wanted to go where I could finish high school and get some college work. I needed more training to be a minister of the gospel." But how? Where was the money to come from? What could he do to get it?

We have to give credit to young Frank that he never stopped trying. About this time he and his brother bought a small store in a country village and Frank got the job of assistant postmaster. After doing this work for a time, he and his brother had a long talk. "We can't keep this up," they agreed.

"What can we do?" asked the brother.

"I know a man who has an old farm which he would trade for the store. We both know farm work. I will live at the farm and work it. It is old and run down. But we can soon make it a better farm."

Frank was as good as his word, and it was not very long before the farm was so much better that the brothers rented it to someone else. At last Frank could see his way open to go to school. He prepared to go in September 1900. Then his father died. Frank knew that his mother needed him. "I will give up my idea of going to school," he said.

"No, my son," answered his mother. "You must keep your purpose of going to school. God has something for you to do."

He entered McPherson College in September. "I did my own cooking and worked at any job I could find," he recalled. These were happy days, busy days. He remembered them with joy. "I loved to preach," he said. "I held evangelistic meetings. I even baptized some of my college classmates. I sang in the college quartet. I played basketball and baseball. But most of all I was interested in the mission-study classes. And soon I knew what I wanted to do with my life. I wanted to be a missionary. I clearly wanted to go to China."

To make sure that nothing would turn him from his purpose of going to China, he let it be known that the woman he would marry must want to be a missionary. And he found her! She was Anna Newland of Kansas. She too wanted to go to China.

In 1908 they were sent by the Church of the Brethren, along with three others, to begin mission work in China. Together they carried on the many kinds of work which missionaries commonly do as needed: teaching, evangelistic preaching, famine relief, assisting refugees, counseling the young church, simple medical work, and whatever else would forward the Kingdom of God. Through the years from 1908 to 1941 they were trusted and beloved leaders in the Chinese church. A great lifework, was it not?

— *Mary Garber*

Brethren Catalyst on the Pacific Coast

George Carl (1867-1940)

You probably know that in chemistry a catalyst is a substance that can be added to a formula to speed up the reaction and which can then be recovered practically unchanged at the end of the reaction. This story of a very busy Brethren preacher will show you that a catalyst may be useful in the work of the church as well as in chemistry.

The early members of the Church of the Brethren on the Pacific coast found a catalyst, dropped it repeatedly into their ongoing mission efforts, recovered it, dropped it in a new spot, and so on to the end with startling results. This catalyst — known as George Carl — always brought the same dependable results which were required of a chemical catalyst.

He was first discovered in Virginia, but, like many other young men, he felt the call of the west winds and migrated to Oregon. He had little, if any, worldly goods, but he had plenty of personal equipment. George Carl was a twenty-five-year-old chunky, energy-packed bundle of dynamite, set to go off somewhere, when the Coquille Valley church in Oregon elected him to the ministry. He began stepping up the results with each contact he made. Hammer and saw served him as often as doctrine and the rules for preaching did, for he was as capable with his hands as he was with his preaching.

Let us watch George Carl at work. "During the summer of 1895, wife and I began a new work in Washington Territory [the country hadn't even been admitted to the Union yet], after a journey of three hundred fifty miles with our horse and buggy. There was only one member in this part of the Territory, and but little money at our disposal. Our opening meeting was well advertised, however, and we expected a fair-sized crowd. There were only eight in attendance. We put our trust in God and did our best 'to be strong and of good courage.' "

Watch Carl speed up the Christian action in that community. When the district board removed him to use him elsewhere two years later, he left a fully organized church with two strong elders in charge. On top of that, he had been forced to remove his four small children from the first town because of smallpox there; so he had started a second church farther away.

Another preacher from Virginia had begun services in Oregon and then had withdrawn, discouraged by the wild country. This mission being about ninety miles from Carl's home, the district board put him on a river boat and sent him up there. He walked fifteen miles back into the forest after he was left on the banks of the Columbia River. After holding meetings in the homes, he repeated them in a schoolhouse thirty miles away, and had to take his converts twenty miles to find enough water to baptize them. Then he walked back to the boat landing. But the boat company was evidently not as punctual with its schedule as George Carl was with his, for he found himself there a day ahead of the steamer.

Believing that killing time was murder, he would have none of that on his hands; so he set out to find a way to fill up the hours. Renting the schoolhouse for the night, he went from door to door advertising a meeting, and in the evening held a preaching service. Since he had paid the rent on the school building for the night, he meant to get the full time out of it. After the service he curled up on one of the rude benches to sleep.

He could dream up better ways of getting about Oregon than that, and he put his dream into action. He built a light wagon so that he could take his wife and his children about the country with him, using his faithful

old buggy horse as the motive power. (Thus George Carl is probably entitled to the patent on today's modern mobile trailer homes!) The Carl family set off to change things in another situation. Meetings were held in seven different homes — one without a roof — and at a sawmill. A dam had to be built across a small stream in order to form a pool; and then he had to wait three days to get enough water to baptize his converts. One of those who were baptized in the water above this dam became a minister in the church which was begun in that community.

After a time he moved on. "I traveled two hundred forty miles with my own conveyance; arrived at the beginning of winter; pitched a tent for my family; rented a church in the center of town; scattered advertising and began preaching." There was not one member of the Church of the Brethren there when George Carl arrived. When he left, according to the reports, there were an organized church; a good, substantial house of worship; three deacons; two ministers; and some seventy active members at Newberg, Oregon.

The big city of Portland, Oregon, had three Brethren members in it when the Carls arrived. Again he pitched a tent for his family, in a vacant lot, rented a place in which to hold services, and began preaching. Christian Catalyst Carl got enough action that he soon sent in this report: "A fine new building, ninety-four regular attendants, five new converts at last night's meeting, and a young sister from Indiana secured as an assistant worker." It would seem that Carl's personal motto — "Trust in God, but get to work and keep at work" — has some merit.

Cars were then becoming common, going farther and faster. Using them, George Carl could now have a hand in building churches from Wenatchee, Washington, on the north to sunny California on the south — and at many points in between.

The Lord must have had need for a catalyst close at hand, for He sent for George Carl. While at a church service one Sunday morning, Brother Carl suddenly ended his very important business of converting people and moving them into action as Christians. The Pacific Coast Region had lost its catalyst. But the entire Church of the Brethren had gained a hero.

— *Geraldine Crill Eller*

From Idols to Christ

Vahaljibhai Nanabhai Bhagat

"Little children, keep yourselves from idols" (1 John 5:21) is the text which inspired a young man to think about the true God. The result was that he has become a follower of Jesus Christ and has led more than twenty-five others out of darkness to his Lord.

The name of the young man is Vahaljibhai Nanabhai Bhagat. His home is at Garda, a small village in Broach District, India. Garda is on the edge of the jungles, ten miles southeast of Netrang, a church center and the location of the railroad station. All the people of Garda are farmers. Vahaljibhai's father has a small farm of about fifteen acres. Vahaljibhai was interested in farming, too, and helped his father in the work from his childhood.

Since Garda had no school, most of the people could not read or write. However, Vahaljibhai went to a nearby village to attend a non-Christian school; but he studied only up to the fourth grade. Later he learned tailoring by paying tuition and serving an apprenticeship under another tailor. Besides farming and tailoring, he runs a small shop seasonally. He is, economically, an independent young man, eager to earn his own livelihood. He works hard at whatever task comes to hand.

Vahaljibhai's father, Nanabhai, was a staunch idol worshiper. He used to fast every Saturday, and was a strong leader of those practicing idol worship. Vahaljibhai took an interest in his father's religion; he was also a faithful worshiper of different idols and was active in the maintenance of idol worship in the village. Later he said: "To get peace in my heart, I worshiped many gods and goddesses, but I found no peace."

From his first contacts with Christians, Vahaljibhai was dead set against them and the Christian religion. He would not even drink water with, or eat with, the Christians. Then when he was twenty years of age, he first came into contact with the teacher-evangelist of the Mandara Christian school. The teacher used to go to Garda to buy things from Vahaljibhai's shop. The result was that they became friends.

Time passed. A new teacher came to the Mandara school. He also took an interest in Vahaljibhai. The teacher visited him now and then, and prayed earnestly for him that he might be led by the Holy Spirit and be able to find the true way of life. In the course of time a copy of the New Testament was given to Vahaljibhai, and he began to read it carefully. He read the four Gospels continuously. Then he changed his method of reading, now opening the New Testament and reading the verse which first came to his sight.

One day, on opening the book, his eyes fell on these words: "Little children, keep yourselves from idols" (1 John 5:21). These words made him think about the true God. A new light came to him, and his life was transformed. He noted that this remarkable day in his life was Friday, June 14, 1952. Having found a new and a certain way, a way of light and life, he stopped idol worship immediately. His father became very angry with him, but Vahaljibhai was at peace despite his father's threats.

Now interested in Christianity, and in search of salvation, he began going to Mandara regularly to attend prayer meetings and church services. He was eager to obtain heavenly peace. After considerable study and careful inquiry, and by the inspiration of the Holy Spirit, he made a firm decision to become a follower of Jesus Christ and accept Him as his Lord and Savior. It was on November 9, 1952, that Vahaljibhai, his wife, and seven others were baptized in their own village.

Now Vahaljibhai devoted his mind and heart to Bible reading and prayer. Feeling the need of Bible study, he began to study the Gospel of John and the Acts of the Apostles through a correspondence course, *Jivan Prakash* (Light of Life), which he finished. Because of Vahaljibhai's patience, effort, and prayer, his father renounced idol worship and came into the church on January 29, 1953.

Vahaljibhai is a considerate, faithful Christian and churchman, one who attends the church services regularly. Because of his good character, non-Christians as well as Christians give him respect. Although he is a humble man, he is fearless in giving his witness and carries the New Testament much of the time for study or sharing with others. He has a spirit of service and hospitality, and takes an active part in all the church activities. He is the leader of midweek worship services, the chairman of the youth committee, the local Sunday-school secretary, and the treasurer of the *Bhajan Mandli* (singing band). In view of his faithful service, the Netrang church appointed him a deacon in 1957. He has been elected as the church's delegate to district meeting several times and has attended district meeting other years as well.

Vahaljibhai is also taking an active part in other social and educational activities. He is a member of the *Gram Panchayat* (village administrative committee) and the chairman of the school advisory committee.

He believes in Christian stewardship. It is said that he has given the tithe of his agricultural produce several times. He faithfully contributes toward the thank-offerings. On occasion, he has borne the entire expense of love feasts held in his village. His wife is also a faithful giver.

Vahaljibhai takes an important part in evangelistic work, giving witness and taking part in the singing band. He uses his talents as "a good and faithful servant" of God. He is living a happy life by the grace of God.

Twenty-nine people in Garda and the surrounding villages have come into the church because of Vahaljibhai's life and witness. Garda is a village with a Christian atmosphere. The place of idol worship is nearly deserted. Christians of Garda are faithful in attending Sunday morning services at Mandara — the women also walk to Mandara and take an active part in the worship. Midweek services are held in Garda, as well as in other villages of the area. Although not well educated, Vahaljibhai is a good Bible student and church worker. When he is in charge of a meeting, he makes careful preparation ahead of time. He is always ready to witness for his faith and to refute opponents.

His life and his testimony are encouragement to people of longer Christian experience and continue to bear fruit for the Lord. We are thankful to our heavenly Father for his life and work, and hope and pray that his life may be a blessing to many more.

— *Premchand G. Bhagat*

Founders of Bethany Seminary

ALBERT C. WIEAND (1871-1954)

EMANUEL B. HOFF (1860-1928)

If ever a boy had reason to say, "I can't?" and to give up hope, it was Albert Wieand. When he was born in Smithville, Ohio, in 1871, the Church of the Brethren had no Biblical seminary to train her ministers. Before he was crippled at the age of fifteen, Albert may have heard someone telling what a good thing it would be if some capable leader would organize a school where Brethren ministers could be trained to serve God and their church more capably. Like other boys and girls, he might have made big plans as to what he hoped to do when he grew up.

However, any such dreams must have died in him after he found that there was no cure for an injury he received in a baseball accident. As often happens, it was just a little thing which changed his entire life and nearly killed him. While he was playing at school a baseball struck him squarely on the spine. Hoping to recover soon, Albert did not then realize that he would not play again. It took many months of lying in bed and listening to the shouts and happy laughter outside before he could face this grim fact. Why were his parents so worried and gentle with him, and why did the doctors stay so briefly? Because there was no hope; he was an invalid — a cripple.

It is not easy to plan on doing great things while sitting in a wheel chair, or to think of ways to serve God when lying in one's bed wracked with pain. Anyway, Albert's easy days were behind him. He could be bitter and hopeless if he chose to; or he could try to walk closer to God. But one thing was certain: that interrupted ball-game was to be the last active game in his life.

Many a time in the ensuing years of invalidism it seemed that God would take him. Doctors did their best and sometimes he improved enough to have a spark of hope. Then tuberculosis set in and his spinal injury was considered incurable.

Hungry to enjoy life among other young people, Albert gritted his teeth and forced himself up from his bed to share their fun and fellowship — only to be driven back to his bed where he writhed in pain as he listened to their laughter and shouts from a distance.

"Is there no hope? Must I always be an invalid?" his soul cried out.

Spurred by his urgency, a specialist made a cast to support his entire body from the waist upward. As he began going around again, friends greeted him happily, saying to him, "Well, Albert, you finally have it licked. Good boy!"

But Albert did not have it licked at all. The strain on his weak back, even when it was supported by the brace, was too much. He developed a cough — a cough flecked with blood. The tuberculosis had spread to his lungs. In numbing despair he went back to bed to die.

Sure now that there was no hope, Albert began preparing to meet God. Seriously he started reading his Bible and praying. He always had been a good boy, but now he had much more time for God than he had when he was active in sports and was going around with his friends. He read his Bible through. Then he read it again — and again. As he prayed, the truth of it began opening to him. This was important, and interesting! Yes, even thrilling! Here he found the assurance he needed. His repentance and profession of faith in Jesus had been sincere. He was sure that the Holy Spirit was present in him. God could give him life in another world just as easily as He gives life here and now. Albert was ready, but did God want him to die now?

Albert had been reading in James 5 how sick people are told to be anointed. He called for the elder of his local church to learn for certain that the Brethren obey this Bible teaching. Finding that they do, he asked to be anointed. While he was willing to leave the outcome to God, he still was young and eager to live. So he prayed, "Lord, if you want to heal me I will give my life to you." Already he had learned that the best life is not to seek pleasure for oneself but to have the deeper joy of walking closely with God.

God heard his prayer. Albert often said later, "He took me up on it." As he was anointed, lying partially helpless in bed, his hands and feet grew warm. He could feel God's healing power at work in him. It did not cease until the day when the doctors examined him and said that he was completely cured.

Now his great concern was not to win a ballgame. It was: "How can I best serve God?" He tried a variety of good things and God seemed to help him in all of them. He taught, and enjoyed teaching. He tried soliciting money to support McPherson College and did well at it. As a young evangelist he went out with Brother J. J. Yoder and the two had eighty converts in a country revival meeting.

Still it seemed to Albert that he did not know enough about people or about speaking. He wanted to learn more.

So he went on to school — first to Moody Bible Institute and then to the University of Chicago. It was here that he formed his deep friendship with Emanuel B. Hoff, who later became his partner in the founding of Bethany Bible School. Living near the university, the Hoffs took Albert in as a roomer. Since they were well-to-do, they soon were helping Albert as much as he would let them. He had free access to Emanuel's large library and the two men spent many hours in exchanging ideas.

Emanuel Hoff was not at all like his serious, dignified friend, who dressed very carefully. An agile, wiry man, he was as lively as a cricket, and had a sense of humor which he often displayed. He liked lively talk and laughter amid a company of people. Half the time he went about in his carpet slippers — and at a time when loafers and sneakers were not in style. His darting, searching eyes missed little, and his keen mind was forever exploring. Especially he liked to explore the Scriptures — a search at which he never tired. Back of all his hearty good humor, E. B. Hoff had a deeply grounded faith in the Lord Jesus Christ and in the Word of God.

In Iowa, when his home congregation learned that Emanuel wanted to be a preacher and consented with some misgivings, they were startled when their cheerful boy-preacher chose the text, "The Spirit of the Lord is upon me. . . ." Many of them had yet to learn that, back of his lighthearted appearance, he was deadly in earnest and all for God. Like A. C. Wieand, he had one great obsession: to find where he could serve God best.

Despite their seeming differences, Albert Wieand and Emanuel Hoff were very much alike. Together they talked, prayed, studied, and traveled, until God revealed His will to them. The decision might have been easier for them if there had not been so many good things to do.

Both were set on some sort of Christian service, and both were sure they needed more schooling. Albert studied in New York and then in Germany, trying to learn more about the human mind and how people could be influenced for God. Emanuel spent more time on the Bible itself, trying to learn well every Bible teaching — for the doctrine of the Brethren was: "Not merely the fundamentals of the gospel, but the *whole* gospel." Always he steered far away from the dangerous practice of marking some of the gospel as "fundamental" and by his silence rejecting any unpopular teaching which he did not care to follow, as many did then and still do.

As he studied, Albert Wieand also taught. At the Bible Teacher's Training School in New York City he became very popular as a teacher. Some of his associates there thought him foolish to try serving among the Brethren when he "could do so much better" in New York. Still the Church of the Brethren needed a Bible school and Albert and Emanuel could not find anyone else who was willing to make the start.

It was on a trip to the Holy Land together that the two men finally made up their minds. They would have to do it themselves. In the little town of Bethany, where Jesus often found shelter and faithful friends, they knelt beneath an olive tree and promised God to start a Bible school and call it Bethany.

In a small, wooden, two-story dwelling at 188 Hastings Street, across the street from the little red brick Church of the Brethren in Chicago, they started their first classes in 1905. Soon they had twenty-five students from several states. So quickly did other Brethren support their adventure in faith that, within four years, they moved to 3435 West Van Buren Street, where they had space to expand.

Bethany grew. Though it seemed to be the school of two men and of God, yet Bethany was founded by many, many more. The wives of the two founders willingly shared in their labors and their sacrifices. Mrs. Ida Wagner Hoff, who was a doctor and a woman of means, gave everything, even her last little home, to support the school. Mrs. Katherine Broadwater Wieand was an able partner with her husband in his many duties. Nor was that all. Young Christian women from many areas came and served as workers at the school and in mission work, often without salary. Farmers and teachers sacrificed to support Bethany for a week or a day or a minute. Students gave of their time to learn about God and about His Word.

Although it was twenty-five years until the church officially took over the management of Bethany, yet the school was an expression of a desire within the church to know more about God and to walk closer with Him. Bethany was fortunate in having founders who checked each new decision on their knees. Their great obsession was to do the will of God, and in His strength. Bethany truly was a work of God. What she will become is of course in the hands of men living today. All of us should support the school, now known as Bethany Biblical Seminary, while we pray that her aims and her work may be as close to the Bible and to its divine source as in the days of Albert Wieand and Emanuel Hoff.

— Roy White

Singing for a Hundred Years

WILLIAM BEERY (1852-1956)

William Beery grew up in a family that liked to sing. His father could be heard singing as he cleared the land, as he built grain bins in the springhouse loft, as he mended shoes. His mother sang when she put the butter in the wooden trough in the springhouse, when she spun thread on the big spinning wheel, and when she wove the thread into cloth on the loom. He quickly learned the melodies that his older brothers and sisters sang when they came home from singing school. As soon as he was old enough he too went to singing school. There was no organ or piano in the Beery home — only an accordion, a harmonica, and a concertina. These instruments were much used.

William was the tenth in a family of thirteen children who lived on a farm in Ohio. When he was a baby the doctor told his mother that he would not live. How mistaken that doctor was! He lived to be almost one hundred four years old.

The last teacher he had in public school, Baxter Shaw, gave a special course of study for those who wanted to teach. William took the course in the summer of 1872 when he was about twenty years old. The next year he was teaching in a schoolroom in Ohio. But the following year he was at work in the sawmill because he needed to earn money to prepare himself better for teaching. The next year he was teaching again.

Word had reached Ohio that a school had been started by the Brethren at Huntingdon, Pennsylvania. It had been in operation for only two years when William Beery decided that he was going to it to try to fulfill his dream of learning more about music and English, and whatever other subjects were being taught there.

Not long after he had gotten started in classroom work in Pennsylvania there was an epidemic of smallpox in the community. It was decided to close the school. Some of the students went to their homes. But William Beery and others felt that if they went the long way back home they might not be able to return. What would they do?

"Not even a dog from Huntingdon would be welcome in the homes of farmers round about," one remarked.

"Let's go to the mountains," another suggested upon hearing of a place in a deep gorge about fifteen miles away where there were several old houses in fair condition.

Fortunately, an old cookstove and a few crude bunks had been left in one of the houses by woodsmen. The three young men set to work to make tables of rough boards from the sawmill and chairs from boughs of sycamore trees entwined by laurel and hickory branches.

When they went to the farmhouses in the area to ask for milk, the women and the children ran from them or looked at them through the crevices of partially opened doors. Eventually, however, they were able to get milk from a farmer or two. (See the story of Martin Grove Brumbaugh, page 136.) Regular hours of study were observed by the three students. In the spring when the school was reopened they went back to continue their studies in the classroom.

The music teacher at the school was Professor J. C. Ewing, whom William Beery in later years called "the pioneer musician in the Church of the Brethren." He helped the young, ambitious, serious student of music to find that which gave him satisfaction for the rest of his life — the joy of singing, composing, teaching music, and worshiping in the use of hymns.

In the fall he was back at Huntingdon as an instructor in vocal music at the school, which later became Juniata College. He continued teaching vocal music for seven years. In the meantime he was studying English and other courses and was graduated in 1882. After teaching in the Middle West for four years he returned to Huntingdon and for many years was a teacher of music in the public schools there. He also directed the college choir, and for thirteen years the choir at the Pennsylvania Industrial Reformatory for Boys.

His composing of hymn tunes began soon after he had his earliest training in music. Two of his hymns were in the first Brethren hymnal (1887) that carried the music scores. When the next hymnal (1901) was published there were a dozen of his compositions in it. Two that are most familiar, "Lo, a Gleam From Yonder Heaven" and "Take My Hand," have been used in the last three Brethren hymnals. Brother Beery helped to prepare two of our hymnals and has had his hymn tunes in four. In the hymnal published in 1951 you can find two which he wrote for this hymnal when he was almost a hundred years old. They are "Savior of My Soul" and "I Will Not Be Afraid." Altogether he composed more than a hundred tunes.

One evening when Brother Beery was walking home from prayer meeting held in the church at Elgin, Illinois, he was talking with the general secretary of the Sunday School Board. The secretary told him that a book of stories of hymns was needed. Brother Beery prepared such a booklet and the following summer *Stories About Hymns* was published. It was used chiefly in church vacation schools and camps. This was the beginning of a larger book entitled *History and Message of Hymns,* put out three years later. William Beery and Margueritte Bixler Garrett worked together on the book.

The active daily work Brother Beery was doing when he retired was proofreading at the Brethren Publishing House. For many years he and his wife, Adaline Hohf Beery, did the first reading on all the publications that went through the printing plant. They must have read hundreds and hundreds of copies of the *Gospel Messenger,* church-school papers, and lesson quarterlies. Mrs. Beery wrote many poems. A number of them were set to music by her husband.

When he was well past eighty years of age Brother Beery accompanied Alvin F. Brightbill and others to music camps and conferences, inspiring younger persons with the joy of song and worship. He was still leading large congregations in hymn singing when he was past ninety years of age.

On his last birthday Brother Beery broadcast on Radio Station WLS, Chicago, as he had done on each birthday for fifteen years. Each year it was the solo, "The Rose of Sharon," that he sang. Before he reached the birthday when he would have been one hundred four years old, April 8, 1956, his voice was silenced by death. He died on January 28, 1956. On his one-hundredth birthday he was a guest soloist on a WGN television program in Chicago. That same year he was a guest soloist at the annual Chicagoland Music Festival luncheon, at which he sang his own composition with the words written by his wife, "Lo, a Gleam From Yonder Heaven," his son Leon accompanying him on the piano. Two years before, he had been a guest on a television program in New York, *Life Begins at Eighty.*

If you have been to Camp Mack, Indiana, you may have seen William Beery's name carved on a memorial stone there. And in the auditorium in the camp, where the murals are hung, you could find his likeness among those of other leaders of the Church of the Brethren. You would recognize him by the white beard and the hands aloft, gracefully leading in hymn singing.

He stood and walked erectly. Even when he had reached a hundred years his body was not bent. When you looked at him you knew that he was sure of something. He was confident because he had a sincere faith in God.

Life was never a burden for him. Always there was something he wanted to do. Composing hymn tunes was an activity for almost as long as he lived. And he wrote many letters. For almost fifty years he had collected data on the Beery family. He wrote and received many letters that brought facts for the history. He and his daughter, Judith Beery Garber, in whose home he lived after Mrs. Beery's death, worked very diligently through a period of years to produce what turned out to be a book of almost eight hundred pages, *Beery Family History*.

Brother Beery was a gentle, kind person. He disciplined himself. He took daily walks, and he ate temperately. He kept his mind alert in creative work. He read the Bible daily. He regularly attended worship on Sunday. His prayers in the church were the sincere expressions of one who lived in the presence of God. Many people in many churches knew him for the Christian gentleman that he was and for what he was able to do in leadership in music even after he had lived longer than the normal life span.

— Edith Barnes

Schoolman and Statesman

MARTIN GROVE BRUMBAUGH (1862-1930)

This may sound like a story which one reads knowing that it did not really happen. But this is a true story — that of a Brethren farm boy who became the governor of his home state.

In 1877 the Brethren Normal College (later named Juniata College) at Huntingdon, Pennsylvania, had just finished its first struggling year of life. Then a smallpox epidemic broke out. The school was forced to close. The students scattered to escape the dread disease. Many thought that the school would never reopen.

Three students from Ohio — one of whom was William Beery, the famous hymn-writer — took refuge some miles away at a lonely place called the Old Forge.

Food was hard to obtain in this out-of-the-way place. One of their teachers asked the owner of the property, a Brethren minister, if his son could not carry food to the students. The father gave his consent. However, the boy was not to associate with the students, because of the danger of infection. Yet, it was not long before the fifteen-year-old lad became a close friend of the students. When the smallpox epidemic was over, and they were free to return to Huntingdon, they urged their new friend and helper to go with them. He was willing, and his father said that he might enter the school in the fall. Thus it was that Martin Grove Brumbaugh went to college.

While yet young, Martin gave evidence of his abilities. Once a traveling salesman dropped into the general store which Martin's father ran. He was struck by the keenness of the boy. He said, "I wouldn't be surprised if that boy would someday be governor of the state!"

His father having been a schoolteacher at one time, Martin was encouraged to read and study. He liked to read books and then tell the stories to his friends when they gathered after the day's tasks.

His memory was amazing. One day he told his brother Frank that he was going to surprise his Sunday-school teachers. They had the practice of giving colored tickets to those boys and girls who could memorize and recite Bible verses. Martin recited one hundred forty-four verses in a row and walked off with all of the tickets!

It was with these qualities that he began college. He took all the courses the school offered, which were not much more difficult than high school courses are today. It was the custom for many college students to spend part of the year teaching school to earn money to go to college in the other months. This is what Martin did. He was sixteen years old when he first taught school.

In college, Martin was an excellent student, even though he had to work part of the time. He was the college janitor to help pay his expenses. He especially liked to speak and debate. These activities were popular among the students then. He was known to make a powerful and convincing speech on one side of an issue, and then argue the other side with equal skill and vigor. Though he graduated in 1881 with a degree in English, he went on to get three more degrees at the college.

In 1884 two eventful things happened. He married Anna Königmacher, one of the Juniata students; and he was appointed superintendent of the Huntingdon County schools. This, at the age of twenty-two! He did so well during the six years in this position that he won the respect of the state school officials. When a request came to them from the State of Louisiana for a leader to improve their school system, M. G. Brumbaugh was recommended. From 1886 to 1891 he traveled all over Louisiana organizing teachers' institutes and giving inspirational lectures.

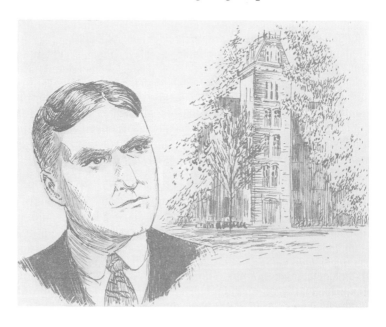

At the age of thirty, Brumbaugh took a surprising step. Unsatisfied with his promising career, he felt the need for advanced education. This is even more remarkable because many in the Church of the Brethren of that day were opposed to higher schooling. He took his family, which now included his children Edwin and Mabel, to Cambridge, Massachusetts, for a year of graduate study at Harvard. Then he went to the University of Pennsylvania. In 1895 he received a Doctor of Philosophy degree. He was the first Brethren to receive this high degree.

At about this time he was called to the presidency of Juniata College. In addition, a new position was created on the faculty of the University of Pennsylvania, and he was appointed a professor. This was a great honor for a young man. For five years he taught his classes and did his work as president of Juniata during the week and then traveled to Philadelphia to teach classes at the university on Saturdays.

Despite this heavy schedule, he found time for preaching sermons and giving speeches all over the state. It was also during this time that his first books were published. Most important among them was his history of the Church of the Brethren — the first real history to be written. He based it on the rich library of Abraham H. Cassel of Harleysville, which Brumbaugh later gave to Juniata College.

The Spanish American War at this time brought changes in the American life. One of them was that the island of Puerto Rico was taken over by the United States. When President McKinley sought an outstanding educator to modernize the schools there, the officials of the University of Pennsylvania recommended M. G. Brumbaugh in recognition of the fine work he had done as a professor. From 1900 to 1902 he took on this new obligation, entering it in the spirit of a missionary.

"El Senor Martino" became known as a friend of the people as they saw his efforts result in great improvements. The number of grade schools increased from six hundred to one thousand, a high school was built, and a teachers' college was begun. More important, though, was the feeling of self-esteem which he taught the people. One Puerto Rican said, "He taught us to hold up our heads; we were not subjects any more of decrepit, decadent Spain, but citizens of the grand young free republic of the United States."

On his return from Puerto Rico, he resumed his teaching at the University of Pennsylvania. Soon this became a full-time job, although he also kept the presidency of Juniata College for some years. His reputation as a schoolman grew with his writing and speaking. He served on an important committee to improve the Philadelphia schools. In 1906 he was chosen as the superintendent of schools for the entire city. He then began that part of his lifework which some people think was his most productive.

He found a poor school system. It was riddled with politics; the teachers were underpaid and unhappy; the buildings and the equipment were old. He took as his motto "A decent seat in a decent school for every child in Philadelphia." A tireless campaign soon made the system one of the best in the country. He succeeded in building new schools, in raising the standards and the pay of the teachers, and in getting the control of the schools from the politicians. He was especially interested in pioneering programs of trade schools, night schools, and playgrounds over the city.

His record was so outstanding that in 1914 he was nominated as the Republican candidate for governor. The victor in the November election, he was the governor from January 1915 to January 1919. When he left for Harrisburg he said, "To give up my lifework, to turn to new duties after thirty-six years of constant service to the schools, is no easy task. My heart will always be with the childhood I love and with the schools in which I have wrought."

One of his first big achievements in the office of governor was the child labor law. Although fought by busiiness interests, this law did much to help children who had been working in mines and factories. He also put through laws for more schooling for working youth and the first law for compensation for workers who were hurt on their jobs.

It fell to the lot of this member of one of the historic peace churches to be the governor of his state when the country entered World War I. His leadership at that time caused some Brethren to feel that he had been unfaithful to the peace teachings of the church.

After his term as governor he taught school in Maine. Then he was asked to return to Juniata College as its president in 1924. Through the years he had given generously to the college. Now he again gave his full time and experience to making it grow. Under his guidance it became recognized as one of the best small colleges in Pennsylvania.

During a brief vacation in North Carolina in March 1930, M. G. Brumbaugh had a heart attack. The assembly of important people and the hundreds of friends who came to his funeral were evidence of the great respect and love which they had for him. He was buried at James Creek in the beautiful surroundings of his boyhood home.

The life of Martin Grove Brumbaugh reads like a romance — from farm boy to governor and professor. Despite the high office and the honors which he achieved, he never lost his love for his church and his college.

— Donald F. Durnbaugh

A Man Who Became Rich

MOY GWONG HAN (1887-1950)

"Honored grandparents, you have graciously cared for my brothers and me since we were small ones," spoke Moy Gwong, a young Chinese. "You have been both father and mother to us since our parents died. Now I am twenty years old. I am a man. I have a wife to support. I have heard that one may become rich in America. I will depart from my beloved China for a short time. Then I will return and care for you, O Gracious Ones."

Moy Gwong Han carried out his plan to come to the United States. He stayed a few years. Then he went back to his home in China. When he died, March 10, 1950, he was rich, too. But not in the way he had first planned — not in gold. He was rich in the souls he had brought into the Kingdom of Jesus Christ. Moy Gwong was the leader of the Church of the Brethren in South China.

This Christian leader was born in Toyshan District on November 27, 1887. His home area is located about one hundred twenty-five miles southwest of Canton and about the same distance west of Hong Kong.

So many people were in that poor and hilly country that it was terribly hard even to live. Imagine twelve hundred people to the square mile trying to farm! For many years, some of the people had been going from South China to other lands to try to make a living for themselves and their loved ones back home. Many of them hoped to return to China after becoming wealthy.

Moy Gwong was one of the many thousands of young Chinese men who came to the United States to make money. But when he met Jesus, his whole life was changed. He made some money and he sent it to China to help his loved ones. But what he wanted most of all was for his people to hear the story of Jesus and His love. And everything he did for the rest of his life was to bring that great desire to pass.

Like many other Chinese immigrants, Moy Gwong found work in a Chinese laundry in Chicago. Also, like many others, he was grateful for the help of friends and kin until he could learn a strange language.

"The first thing you must do is to learn the English language," he was told by friends. "Come with us to the Chinese Sunday school. Here you will be taught to speak English. You will meet good friends and you will have a good time."

At first he went to a Baptist Sunday school, but soon his friends invited him to the Brethren Sunday school organized by Bethany Bible School on West Hastings Street. Here he found his life's work. And the Church of the Brethren found a great leader.

"I started teaching Moy Gwong before he knew any English," said his teacher, Franklin J. Byer, then a student at Bethany. "As soon as we could, we began reading the New Testament."

It was not long before a friend said to his teacher, "Brother Byer, Moy Gwong wants to be baptized."

"Tell him that we will learn more about the New Testament and what baptism means," said the Sunday-school teacher, "and he can be baptized later."

The next two Sundays, Moy Gwong was absent. But

he had a good Sunday-school teacher who went after him. He wasn't easy to find. "Try other Chinese laundry," he was told again and again, for Moy Gwong had changed places of work.

"I was about ready to give up," said Moy Gwong when at last his teacher found him. But he came back to the Sunday school. And when he was baptized, one of the first things he said was "I want my wife to learn of the Christian faith." So it was arranged for her to go to school in China where she, too, after a time, accepted Christ as her Savior.

It wasn't long until Moy Gwong knew what he wanted to do. "I want to tell my people about Jesus," he declared. His course was set.

But he kept on working in the laundry about a year. Then he quit the laundry business forever. "I must get more education," he said. Because his parents had died when he was quite young, he had had only two years of secondary school. But he had been taught a trade.

He spent three years in Bethany Bible School and the Y. M. C. A. College in Chicago. Then he went to Manchester College. In 1920, he was graduated. He had learned the English language besides getting a college education.

But he did not go around all the time with his nose in a book! It's true that he was a good student, but he was a good friend, too. The teachers liked him and the students liked him.

"I remember him well," said one who was in college with him. "It was wonderful to know him. The way he lived, one knew he loved God."

Before he was graduated from college, he was ordained to the Christian ministry. "I gladly responded, and considered it to be a call from God," said Moy Gwong.

From then on, he spent most of his week ends and vacations in church work and in earning money to help support his family in China. He never forgot them.

He preached in churches in many states, especially in Ohio, Indiana, Illinois, Iowa, Michigan, Pennsylvania, Virginia, Maryland, and Tennessee. In one month in the summer of 1918 he visited thirty-seven churches. Many people learned to know him. They loved him and he loved them. He helped organize a Chinese Sunday school in Seattle, Washington, and he helped in the Chicago Sunday school. He spent about ten years of his Christian life in the United States.

When Moy Gwong went back to China in 1920, he was sent by the Mission Board of the Church of the Brethren to become the pastor of the church started by the missionaries, Brother and Sister Elgin S. Moyer and Sister Martha B. Shick. He later became the principal of the school also.

"God directed him to come back to his people," said his wife. "His friends came to congratulate him, thinking he had made a great deal of money. In answer he said, "I have brought back only Jesus."

Yes, Moy Gwong was rich. And famine or war or death itself cannot destroy his riches.

— *Mary Garber*

All the Credit to God

IDA C. SHUMAKER (1873-1946)

The trees on the Pennsylvania hillsides were gold and bronze when a little girl was born to Alexander and Lydia Shumaker at Meyersdale in October 1873. She was given a loving welcome into the family and was named Ida Cora.

When Ida was old enough to go to school she was happy to walk along with her three sisters and her two brothers. She liked school very much; in it she was always learning something fresh and interesting. In fact, all through her life the schoolroom was one of her chief joys.

In the home Ida had her tasks to do. And she gladly did her share, along with her brothers and sisters. She loved the beautiful world about her. She liked to play in the sunshine, to run in the woods, to gather flowers, to throw snowballs, to wade in the water. But her curiosity and her spirit of adventure sometimes led her into trouble. One day she and her smaller sister nearly drowned. Ida never forgot that experience and it helped her to be more careful.

For Ida, Sunday was a very happy day. She loved the Sunday school and the services in the church. It was always a treat to meet her friends there. And although it was unusual it was not surprising that she was asked to teach a primary class when she was only eleven years old. If anything could be more fascinating than teaching she did not know what it was. When Ida was fourteen years old she joined the church and was baptized. Wanting to help in the church work wherever she could, she was always doing something helpful.

When Ida was only sixteen years of age she began teaching in the public schools. And how she enjoyed it! She loved to be with the children and they enjoyed being with her. To them she was more than a teacher; she was "Aunt Ida." People said that she was a "natural-born" teacher and they considered her a very successful one. Her county superintendent of schools was greatly pleased with her work.

All who knew Ida thought it was wonderful the way she took hold of her work and carried it on. Not only was she teaching in both Sunday school and public school. She also traveled among the churches of Western Pennsylvania to help them with their Sunday-school work. The people thought that she would always be with them to help them.

But it was not to be that way. In those days when she was busy in the church and in the school something happened which changed the rest of her life. A call to go to India as a missionary came in a letter from the General Mission Board of the Church of the Brethren. This letter caused her to think very seriously. She thought it was almost too wonderful for words that she might actually become a missionary. And yet she felt that she was not good enough. Then too she wondered whether she could give up the chance of having a home of her own in America. And when she talked with her doctor about living in India he told her she could not live more than six months in that hot climate.

For two full years Ida Shumaker fought a battle within herself. One day she would think that her answer must be yes. Then another day she would be sure it must be no. Finally she wrote to the Mission Board saying that she could not go. She thought she had settled the matter. But one evening as she sat alone having her devotions she somehow *knew* that God wanted her in India. There was no more doubt in her mind. She wrote another letter to the Board, saying that she would go.

Ida's first home was to be at Bulsar, one hundred twenty-five miles north from Bombay.

At once she began to study the strange Gujarati language. She could smile at the people without knowing their language; and they could smile at her. But she knew she had to learn to talk with them. This meant much hard work, but she knew how to study. She learned the language well.

As in Pennsylvania, so in India, Ida was soon teaching classes of girls and women. Each Sunday she was busy in the church and the Sunday school. She not only taught the women, but she also taught them how to teach. She prepared primary lessons for the *Gujarati Sunday School Quarterly* and she translated English articles into that language. All her days were filled with humble and often difficult duties. The women and the schoolgirls looked to "Ida Miss Saheb" as to an older sister and a mother.

Children were always a special delight to Ida, whether they were the brown-skinned boys and girls of India or the fair-skinned children of the missionaries. She enjoyed giving them pleasant surprises and entertaining them with stories. All the missionary children who knew her remember how she "took their picture" during the missionary conferences. She would ask them to stand in line. Then, with a large tin box under one arm, she would pass down the line giving to each child a handful of candy — the hard, round kind. Then she excused them with laughter and smiles. No wonder all the children loved her and called her Aunt Ida.

It was fortunate that from early childhood Ida had enjoyed being out of doors. In India she often walked many miles to some village school — sometimes in the rain and the mud and sometimes in the sunshine and the deep dust. There were many times when she forded flooded

streams. It took courage to sit in an oxcart when the oxen had to swim and all she could see of them was their noses. Then there were times when accidents happened. Once she was spilled from a two-wheeled cart. There were dark nights, too, when Aunt Ida and the ox-driver traveled through pouring rain for hours on their way home from the villages. And she had close calls with snakes! All these things she met bravely and with humor, for she believed that she was on the path of duty. Ida Shumaker really had a sense of humor. She saw the funny side of nearly every incident. Even when the joke was on herself she made a jolly story out of it so that others might enjoy it.

Added to Aunt Ida's zest for life and her enthusiasm for her work was her deep desire to do God's will. Her faith was great. Whether before large groups when on furlough in America or in a tiny village tucked back in the Indian jungle, she believed that she was being led of God. Whether she was mothering the girls of an orphanage or a school or was manning the Khergam mission station, she gave God the credit. She saw the results of her efforts as work which God had wrought.

Contrary to the doctor's statement that she could not live more than six months in India, Miss Shumaker lived and worked there for thirty-five years. In February 1946 she said her last farewell to her beloved India and was laid to rest in the quiet roadside cemetery near the Bulsar church. The Shumaker Memorial church at Khergam and the loving memories of those whose lives she touched for good are her lasting memorials. She needed — and she would have wanted — no others.

— *Anetta C. Mow*

Martyrs for Christ in China

MINNEVA NEHER (1896-1937)

ALVA HARSH (1910-1937)

MARY HARSH (1903-1937)

Our first Brethren missionaries to a foreign land were sent in 1876. During the years between then and 1937 well over two hundred missionaries were sent to various countries. In traveling to and from their fields of work and in carrying on their duties they traveled tens of thousands of miles without a tragic death occurring among them. And then in that latter year Minneva Neher and Alva and Mary Harsh mysteriously disappeared in China and were never heard from again.

Minneva Neher was in her second term of work in Shansi Province. The Harshes were just ready to begin their service in China. The three were thoroughly in love with their work and were deeply consecrated to their Lord. They were highly and lovingly thought of by their fellow missionaries and by their Chinese associates.

Minneva Neher was born in Inglewood, California, in October 1896. William H. and Lottie Flory Neher were her parents. As a little girl she learned to love the church and all its activities. While still very young she decided that she wanted to become a missionary. She never forgot how deeply thrilled she was when she heard her cousin, Frank Crumpacker, talk about going to China.

This hope of becoming a missionary grew stronger and stronger during the days when she was in college. After leaving college she went to Chicago to attend Bethany Bible School. In order that she might be of the greatest help to the people with whom she would work she took some nurse's training also. She wanted to be efficient in all her work.

In 1924 she sailed for China. First she lived in Peking (now called Peiping) where for two years she studied the difficult Chinese language. As she studied she learned much by teaching a Sunday-school class in Chinese. In addition to learning the language by using it in this way, she was learning to know the Chinese people.

Minneva was assigned to work in the town of Show Yang. This village had a fascination all its own for her. It was tucked far back in the hills. The people of Show Yang had seen few "Western foreigners." But, even so, its history held some sad memories. About twenty-five years before Minneva went there, the terrors of the Boxer Uprising had been felt there. This was a short war in which the Chinese had tried to force all foreigners out of their land. Some English Baptist missionaries had had to give up their work in Show Yang. Minneva was now living in one of the houses once occupied by those missionaries. The village and its needy people were very dear to her.

From the day Minneva moved to Show Yang she was a busy missionary. She traveled many long, weary miles on the backs of donkeys. On rough roads — or on no roads at all — they climbed up and slid down the hills and made their way through the valleys. She and her Chinese helper, a Bible-woman, visited in homes all over that area, carrying the message of Christ's love. As the principal of the mission school she had many duties. She taught classes in both the school and the Sunday school. She led worship

152

services and gave Christian messages, all in the Chinese language. She called in the homes of the poor, helping the mothers and the children. Many times she took some of her own dresses and remade them into clothes for babies and small children.

Minneva's last two years at Show Yang were very difficult ones. The whole country of China was disturbed. Part of the time the people in Shansi Province were under Japanese rule. Bands of wandering soldiers annoyed the people. Many of the Chinese lost their homes. More and more sorrow was added to their poverty and helplessness. All of this was a heavy burden on Minneva's heart.

It was during these war-stricken days that the new missionaries, Alva and Mary Harsh, moved to Show Yang. They arrived in June 1937. Minneva shared her home with them, and they were to serve along with her.

Alva was born in West Virginia in September 1910 to Jesse and Effie Harsh. Mary was born in August 1903 to Brother and Sister Charles Hykes of Maryland. The stories of their early days sound much alike. Both attended church and Sunday school regularly. Both of them were twelve years old when they were baptized and became members of the Church of the Brethren. Both were eager to receive a good education and to become workers in the church.

Then came college days. Alva and Mary were students together in Elizabethtown College in Pennsylvania and later they went to Bethany Biblical Seminary in Chicago. It is easy to see that they became well acquainted with each other at these schools. They were active students and hard workers. Both helped in the various activities connected with the seminary and the church. No matter what they were doing, they were serving the church at that time and were being prepared for efficient work in the future.

At the early age of seventeen Alva had been elected to the ministry in his home church. Soon after their marriage in June 1934, Alva and Mary moved to Petersburg, West Virginia, to serve three churches in that community. For two years they gave themselves to the people of these churches; and the members and the neighbors loved them.

In 1936, Alva and Mary, along with two other missionaries, went to China. As with all new missionaries, they found that their first task in a strange land was to learn the language. They went to Peiping to live and to attend the College of Chinese Studies. On their first Christmas in China they had the very happy experience of visiting three of the Brethren mission stations in Shansi Province for two weeks. During those weeks they got their first close look at the work that had been assigned to them. From then on they looked forward still more eagerly to the time when they would be ready for this work.

With their study in Peiping completed, the Harshes moved to Show Yang and settled in their new home. Then they felt that their missionary work had at last begun. Their letters to their parents and their friends in America were filled with the joy they were finding in their work. However, in the midst of their happiness they were unhappy about the poverty and the sorrow they found everywhere among the Chinese people. Many of the Chinese people were wretchedly poor. This extreme poverty was found in both the town of Show Yang and the surrounding villages. Everywhere the Harshes went, their hearts were filled with sympathy for these suffering people.

Added to all this, and in many ways connected with it, there was fighting in the land. Scouting planes flew overhead, bombs were dropped, and armed soldiers some-

154

times came into the town. Everyone lived in fear. More than a hundred Christians and their relatives came to the mission compound for shelter. Every day Alva went about the compound and into the hospital. Often he followed the oxcart to haul coal, which was desperately needed. Services were held among this group of people. Minneva and the Harshes felt that these conditions gave them a special opportunity to preach the gospel. In every possible way, the three missionaries gave themselves freely in service to the Chinese people.

Then came December 2, 1937. A curtain of mystery has surrounded that day. However, it is known that on that evening, as Minneva, Mary, and Alva were having their evening prayers, a messenger came to their home. This messenger asked them to go with her to a Chinese home in which, she said, the people were having a quarrel. This house was said to be about a half mile from the missionaries' home.

In response to this call for help, the three left their home and went outside the gates of the compound. Doubtless these trusting missionaries never knew just what was happening. We know now that this request for help was a well-laid treacherous trap to lure them outside their home and into the hands of those who sought their lives. They were never seen by the little group of Chinese Christians again. No one knows how death came to them.

Their lives had been brief but they were filled with good work for the uplift of their fellow men and the advancement of the Kingdom of our Christ. They gave all they had. What more can we, or need we, say?

— Anetta C. Mow

A Wheel-Chair Ministry

MYRA BROOKS WELCH (1878-1959)

It's a long story. Some of it has been told before; but it deserves to be told again.

Myra Brooks Welch grew up in what she called a singing family. In her childhood home were the reed organ, the violin, the guitar, the banjo, the accordian, the mouth organ, and the jew's harp. Her home was a musical center for her family and their friends. For many of their weekday evening and Sunday afternoon "sings" she was the organist. Also, she learned to play the guitar and later the piano.

This love for, and ability in, instrumental music was carried with her, after her marriage, into her own home. Then, while she was busy caring for her home and her family, illness came and her whole life was changed. She had to give up her instrumental music because her hands became crippled with arthritis.

But the arthritis could affect only her body; it could not smother the music in her soul. She needed to find a new expression for that music. Then she began writing poetry, in which, up to that time, she had had no real interest. And, much to her surprise, those who read or heard her poetry liked it. To her further surprise, within a few years she was one of the best known poets in the Church of the Brethren. Some of her poems have become widely known in this country and in other countries.

Having lived in different parts of the United States — Illinois, Nebraska, Kansas, Oregon, and California — Mrs. Welch both saw and enjoyed many different kinds of natural beauty. Her love of the beautiful, which is seen in many of her poems, is well summed up in these lines:

> Each day I see some lovely thing
> That lifts my heart and makes it sing.

Mrs. Welch spent over twenty years in her wheel chair, following more than twenty other years of physical suffering. But her mind was free to go all over the world. And it did — seeing the beauty, the ugliness, the joys, and the sorrows of human life. These in turn found a place in her poetry.

> What need have I to roam afar
> When books upon my knee
> And windows with a wide outlook
> Can bring the world to me?

At the same time, she found love for and faith in the God whose world this is.

> Thy word is written in the heavens, Lord.
> There it is traced in language each may read
> No matter what his color be, or creed;
> It shines for each and all with one accord.

In this way, year after year, she shared with others the joys she found in life. Thousands of copies of her three books of poetry are in homes and libraries. Her poems are printed in various magazines and are sometimes reprinted in books other than those published by the Brethren Press. They are also often used in sermons, lectures, and worship services. The radio has brought them to many people who would not otherwise hear them.

These poems are still carrying to others Mrs. Welch's

love of beauty, her deep faith in the goodness and the love of God, and her interest in other people. From that wheel chair in La Verne, California, there spread over these years a ministry that blessed countless thousands. Who can say

that this ministry was not the richer because of the handicap under which Mrs. Welch lived and worked? Or that it was not the greater because she turned from instrumental music to poetry?

Possibly the readers and hearers of Mrs. Welch's poems would have loved and appreciated them even more had they known how she did her typing of them. Her hands too badly deformed to type in a normal manner, she found other methods. Holding a pencil in each hand, she pressed the typewriter keys with the rubbers on the pencils. Thus, slowly and painfully, she placed on paper the songs God had placed in her heart.

Her best known poem, "The Touch of the Master's

Hand," has traveled over much of the world. Its first two stanzas tell of an old violin, battered and scarred, that was about to be sold at public auction for three dollars. But after it had been played by a skilled violinist it was sold for three thousand dollars. Its real value had been shown by the touch of a master's hand. The final stanza is as follows:

> And many a man with life out of tune,
> And battered and scarred with sin,
> Is auctioned cheap to the thoughtless crowd,
> Much like the old violin.
> A "mess of pottage," a glass of wine;
> A game — and he travels on.
> He is "going" once, and "going" twice,
> He's "going" and almost "gone."
> But the Master comes, and the foolish crowd
> Never can quite understand
> The worth of a soul and the change that's wrought
> By the touch of the Master's hand.

Since this sketch was written and set into type, Mrs. Welch's crippled hands have quit their difficult typing of her songs of faith, love, and courage. Her wheel-chair ministry has, in a sense, ended. But, in the providence of God, that ministry will continue for many a year as the poems of this much-loved musician-turned-poet are read, reread, and reread yet again.

— Ora W. Garber

A School Named in Her Honor

GRACE HILEMAN MILLER (1878-1955)

The children were so excited they could scarcely sit still. That tomorrow was the beginning of Christmas vacation was excitement in itself, but today — today the big yellow school bus was coming to take them to the new school building! For several months they had been looking forward to the time when the building would be completed and they would be moving. And now the time had come. Today they would take their books and supplies. And then at the close of the vacation they would begin classes there.

At last word came that the bus was waiting outside. The short trip across town was soon over, but not the excitement. The rooms were beautiful. The children exclaimed as they explored them and admired the bright colors, the shining new tables and chairs, the wonderful place in which to work. They could almost wish they weren't having a vacation, for it was going to be hard to wait two more weeks before they could begin work in this beautiful new building — the Grace Miller Elementary School.

Who was Grace Miller, and why should this new school in La Verne, California, have been named for her? The teachers in the school knew, for several of them had known and worked with her. Most of the children were too young to remember Mrs. Miller, but her story was one that the boys and girls could appreciate. So it was that the third-grade students found written on their chalkboard as they came into the room, "Welcome to Grace Miller School." And so it was that they spent some time in discussing why this name had been chosen for their new school.

Grace Hileman Miller had not always lived in La Verne, but fifty-three of her seventy-seven years were spent there. It was there that she met and married John L. Miller. Mr. Miller owned a grocery store in La Verne. Mrs. Miller clerked in the store and helped to deliver grocery orders. She did not drive a car, but she did ride a bicycle; so she made deliveries on her bicycle.

Grace Miller loved her church and she loved children. It was no surprise, then, that she soon gathered together a group of children who met with her at the church on Sunday afternoons. This group was called the Mission Band.

Mrs. Miller continued teaching in the Sunday school of the La Verne church for many years. Most of this time she taught a primary class and was the primary department superintendent. She was a wonderful storyteller. She had a large collection of stories, but many of those she told were her own. She had one for every occasion. She also shared them with others across the Brotherhood by writing for the church publications.

Because she so much enjoyed teaching, Mrs. Miller wanted to help others to teach. Many young people became interested in teaching because of her. Some she helped through having them assist her in her teaching. Others she taught through leadership training courses and demonstration classes for Brethren teachers and those of other churches. Because she was interested in helping others to teach, she gladly accepted when she was asked by the District of Southern California and Arizona to become the district director of children's work. For six years she traveled many miles and spent many hours in this work. She was a leader in many vacation church schools during this time and in the years that followed. Mrs. Miller was a camp leader, too. For many years she taught children's classes at the Camp La Verne family camp. She continued to do this even after she was in her seventies.

Her interest reached beyond her own church to people of other denominations and other races. At one time she taught English to Japanese-speaking and Spanish-speaking persons who wished to become American citizens. For about thirty years she taught her class of primaries at her own church, then left to ride her bicycle or to walk six blocks to teach a Sunday-school class at the Emmanuel Presbyterian church, the Protestant church for the Spanish-speaking people of La Verne — a church which Mrs. Miller had helped to organize.

Mrs. Miller's Sundays were busy ones, but so were the weekdays. Not only was she the homemaker for Mr. Miller and their four children as they were growing up, but she worked with children during the week, also. She helped to organize the Y. W. Buds, a junior girls' organization of the Young Women's Christian Association, and was their leader for twenty-six years. These Y. W. Buds, many of them Mexican-American girls, learned from Mrs. Miller the art of sharing. Many a sick child, shut-in adult, or lonely person was made happy by a visit or a gift from the Buds.

Mrs. Miller thought not only of those children who were in her classes and club groups, but she found time to work with the YWCA board which planned for and guided work with girls over the whole valley.

When her own children were in school, Mrs. Miller joined in school activities. She continued that interest long after her children were grown. She remained active in the parent-teacher association all her life, as well as in other community activities.

Mrs. Miller continued her college studies after her marriage, and in 1914 she earned the Bachelor of Sacred Literature degree from La Verne College. In 1951 she was honored by the college for her church and community leadership. Again in 1953, the college honored her with the title, Community Builder, in appreciation for her fifty years of service to the people of La Verne.

Mrs. Miller's life was ended by an automobile accident on Christmas Eve, 1955. Though her life was over, her influence remained. The many people whom she had taught and with whom she had worked through the years could not forget what she had done for her church and for her community. How better could they honor her than to name the new school in her memory?

The third graders on that first Monday in January could not really understand all that the life of Mrs. Miller had meant to those who knew her, but one boy stated it simply when he wrote in his storybook: "Our new school is the Grace Miller School. It is a nice school. It is called the Grace Miller School because Grace Miller was a good lady. She liked boys and girls."

— *Margaret Lininger*

Pioneers of the Nigerian Church

H. STOVER KULP (1894 —)

RUTH ROYER KULP (1896-1924)

CHRISTINA MASTERTON KULP (1896-1952)

He was "Uncle Rev" to the small fry. It was fun when he came around. Harold Stover Kulp has played fond uncle to swarms of nieces and nephews, real and pretend, on three continents. He has won a lasting and unique place in the hearts of the Brotherhood at home and of the Nigerian people to whom he is giving a lifetime of loving service.

It was September 1894, and the Aaron Kulp family was busy on their large and prosperous farm in eastern Pennsylvania. There was much to do: the last of the crops were to be brought in; the series of special meetings at the Coventry church would be held soon; and Naomi Tyson Kulp was expecting her fourth baby any minute.

Brother Wilbur Stover had just been appointed to go out to India to open the mission work there for the Church of the Brethren. His meetings throughout the Brotherhood were causing great interest in the Christian's part in carrying out the Great Commission.

On September 29, the new baby arrived. "We'll call him Stover," decided his mother as she consecrated him to a life of service in the church.

164

The rolling Chester County countryside was familiar to young Stover Kulp as he walked more than a mile each way to the Belleview country school and even farther to the Coventry Church of the Brethren, where, on Thanksgiving Day, 1906, he was baptized by Ira C. Holsopple. Stover hunted the fertile fields and woods, trapped along the streams, and canoed and fished in the Old Schuylkill Canal. Little did the family guess that he would one day hunt elephants in the wilds of Africa.

Stover was small for his age. In connection with his size, his older sister, Ruth Kulp Glazier, remembers his work in their father's farm machinery business: "At that time, farm machinery came 'knocked down' to save hauling costs, and had to be assembled by the dealer. Stover was handy, and on Saturdays and in summer would help Father assemble the machinery. He could get in, under, or over to put in bolts and parts."

Decades later, his ingenuity came into further service as he devised refrigeration equipment to safeguard the food for his family under the broiling African sun.

Stover took an active part in school and church activities, especially in the plays and the programs that were the basic form of community entertainment in those wonderful pre-TV days. His elementary teacher, B. Curtis Rinehart, recollects that he was "not only a studious boy, but an unusual student." Others remember him as active in all community affairs, and quite jolly. When he was graduated from the East Coventry high school, in 1908, he "appeared like a ten-year-old in his short pants."

Appearances, however, are sometimes deceiving. Stover graduated from normal school too young to teach in the Pennsylvania public schools. But he accepted a position on the faculty of the Carter Junior Republic, a school in character building and citizenship for wayward boys, near Pottstown. He was no older than some of the troubled and trouble-making boys who had been sent there because of their difficulties with the law. The year before, they had run two teachers out.

In May 1915, Stover accepted the call to the ministry in his home church. That fall he entered Juniata College at Huntingdon, working his way as a student teacher. In his sophomore year he joined the Student Volunteer Movement, committing himself to foreign missionary service. His college days, to graduation in 1918, were filled with volunteer group service, YMCA, debating, basketball, and track. He was an outstanding member, and the definite leader of, any group.

And he found, in those days, inspiration, fellowship, companionship, and love in the kindred spirit of Neta Ruth Royer.

"It is time to go, Mother," called Galen Royer of Elgin, Illinois, to his wife, Anna Miller Royer, as the time for meeting neared.

Bess walked primly out to West Chicago Street; Dan raced around the corner of the large house; and Kathren ran down the porch steps.

Mother Royer picked up Baby John and looked around. "But where are the girls?" she exclaimed. Off flew the family in search of little Ruth and Jo, always together, dressed alike, often mistaken for twins. At last they were discovered down in the basement, behind the stairs, dressed in their Sunday-best, having a delightful taffy-pull in the keg of sorghum molasses!

Ruth was a merry little girl, loved by all who knew her. At the age of eleven, very early for those days, she was baptized by her father into the Elgin Church of the Brethren. She attended the Elgin public schools, then

166

went to nearby Wheaton College, and later was graduated from Juniata College with the class of 1919.

During the Christmas vacation of her sophomore year, instead of going back to Elgin she stayed in Pennsylvania to save traveling expenses. On visiting a friend, she found

the entire family down with the flu. She did all the farm chores, took care of the family, and nursed them back to health before the end of her precious two weeks' vacation.

Ruth had a deep concern for the poor, the weak, and the sick. Suffering touched her strongly. She had a deep desire to serve God and man as a medical missionary. She studied medicine at the University of Pennsylvania, and then, as Mrs. H. Stover Kulp, she continued her studies at Livingston College in London while her young husband went on to open a new mission station in Nigeria.

The opening of the station at Garkida by Brethren Kulp and Helser is described in Stover Kulp's words:

"March 17, 1923, was a great day for us. As the light

167

of the dawning sun was breaking over the eastern hills, we had the ground breaking service for the first house to be built by the Church of the Brethren in Africa. When we knelt to pray, the sun had not yet risen, but, after prayer, its glorious light was beaming full upon us."

Later that fall, Ruth joined her husband on the mission field. Together they studied the language, held services, and ministered to the spiritual and physical needs of the people. They cleared land, put up buildings, and started the compound that was to become an educational, medical, and religious center for the Bura people.

But their service together was brief. Less than a year later, the little congregation that had come to love her so quickly stood with Stover Kulp beside the fresh graves of his young wife and their tiny son on the hillside above Garkida.

Of such love and sacrifice was born Stover's life of service to the Church of the Brethren mission in Nigeria.

It was in the Midlothian region of Scotland, known as Sir Walter Scott territory, that Christina Masterton was born in 1896. This area, bordering the rugged eastern Scottish coast, was a favorite vacation and resort country for many Europeans as well as the native Scots.

Her talent with delicate and subtle sounds contributed later to her outstanding success in learning the Margi and Bura (Nigerian) languages, for, in her long and active service to the Nigerian people under the Church of the Brethren, she translated many articles, hymns, and books, including the New Testament. Her ear for music enabled her to set down the native tunes, and then she composed suitable verses to become early hymns for this pioneer Christian church in the African bush.

Christina had spent a strenuous term at Livingstonia

mission in the lion country of Northern Rhodesia under the United Presbyterian Church of Scotland, and was on furlough taking special work in Bantu languages in the School of Oriental Languages and Cultures in the University of London, when she met Stover Kulp in the fall of 1926. She went to hear him preach; they were both staying at the Foreign Missions Club; they shared a love of humanity, a dedication for missions in general, and a background of African experience in particular. And so it came about that one foggy November afternoon on an upper deck of a tramcar in the heart of London, they decided to continue their mission service as a team.

The Kulps were more than pioneers in a physical sense. Together, they helped build a literature for a people whose language had never been written before. They wrote a first reader and taught adults, as well as children, the magic of the printed page. In this way, the Word of God through the teachings of Christ gradually came to the Nigerian people of the Brethren mission area.

One time, after they had been talking with a blind man, he asked them when the "white strangers" would arrive. "We told him *we* were the white folks," Christina wrote home, "and he said, 'Why, I thought you were Margi!' So we rejoiced in knowing that at last we were understood and had become as one of themselves."

Now Christina Kulp rests in the hedge-lined plot on the Garkida hillside while the work she did, the words she wrote, and the songs she sang live on, cherished in the lives and the hearts of her beloved Nigerian people.

Nigeria, Africa, the Church of the Brethren, and the world — all are richer for the lives, the service, and the loves of the Nigerian pioneers, the Kulps.

— Frances Holsopple Fenner

The Preacher Prince

MAI SULE (1920 —)

"Oh, won't you come along with me to my Father's house . . . ?"

Do you hear those lusty singers all around you, making joyful noise unto the Lord? Those are the members of the Virgwi congregation, in Nigeria, in once-darkest Africa.

Do you see that black, shiny-skinned man standing there in front of us, leading the song, beads of perspiration standing on his forehead? Notice how he manages to lead us in our singing, with a rhythmically swinging left hand, while his right hand points to heaven, to show us where his "Father's house" is? Do you see that happy smile upon his face, as if to proclaim that to praise God is a great joy? That's Mai Sule, the African prince. He's the pastor here, you know — the first Nigerian to become an elder in the Church of the Brethren.

What! You don't know Mai Sule? Come on over here and sit down while he preaches one of his shorter sermons. See him standing there behind the pulpit, opening up his little old goatskin bag. He keeps his books in that, and also his pencils, chalk, erasers, and . . . who knows what else? Look! He is taking something out of the bag. It's a sprinkling bottle full of water. Now what? Listen!

"Today my sermon is about sin. Sin is dangerous. Don't play with it. Once there was a man who used all

170

his great wealth to put a fine, thick, thatched grass roof on his big house. As he sat in his house, he wondered if the roof would burn. So he got a gourd full of water and set it on his stool. Then he took a red coal from the fire and set his roof aflame. A simple matter. He just splashed water on it from the gourd, like this."

Look out! Mai Sule has taken that sprinkling bottle and is splashing water on us to show us how the fire was put out. Now he is talking again.

"He put the fire out, easily. So he thought he would try again, and this time he let it burn a little better before he sprinkled."

Look out! More water from the sprinkling bottle. We shouldn't have sat so close to the front! More story (or more sermon — which is it?):

"This was an interesting game. The man tried it again . . . and again . . . and again, each time splashing water on his roof from the gourd, to put out the fire. And then he tried it once more. He reached for the gourd, put in his hand to splash the water and. . . ."

Look! Mai Sule is trying to sprinkle but the water is all gone. The water is all gone!

"No more water. The roof — that beautiful, new, thatched-grass roof — was burned up completely. My people, let this be a lesson to us. We can't play with sin."

Now you are getting acquainted with Mai Sule, aren't you? Let's have another look. They are having a big drama out at the Virgwi church today. It is March 17, Founders' Day, the day the Church of the Brethren first came to Garkida, back in 1923. Their drama will show the "before and after" of the coming of the gospel.

Kai! Look at that witch doctor! I wonder how they got a real witch doctor to put on a show in a Christian church! Look . . . he has all his paraphernalia: the old rag clothes, the baboon-skin mat on which to sit; the wildcat skin hanging down his back. He has the horns, the teeth, the skin bags, the turtleshell, the seeds and cotton and thread, the bones and stones, the pots and gourds, the horn-headed staff. It almost scares me to look at him.

That woman has come to him with her problem.

"Oh, great sir, I have been married for many years. But the gods have never given me any children. I am afraid I must have a demon. I'll pay you anything if you will chase away the demon."

Hear how grave and solemn is the voice of the witch doctor. "Madam, this is serious indeed. You have not one, but seven, devils at work in you. It will be hard work to chase them out. You will have to pay seven rolls of cloth."

There, the frantic woman has paid the fee, and the witch doctor is going to work. Listen to his incantations. See how he circles the woman's head with his magical staff. See the scowl on his face. Now he is taking a wand of shafa leaves and striking the woman with it. He's chasing away the demons. What a farce! Why did they let him come into our Christian church?

But wait! That's no witch doctor. It's Pastor Mai Sule! What is he saying?

"My people, all this is lies. The only truth is in Christ Jesus — He who sent the church to us in 1923."

But you can't know Mai Sule . . . not really. You can just get glimpses of the depth of his consecration to Christ, which motivates his song-leading, his preaching, his drama, his life. Let me tell you more about him.

He is a prince, really. He is a man with royal blood. He was named after the chief of the village-in-exile where he was born — Mai (King) Sule (Solomon): King Solomon. His father and almost all his clan are Muslims; they could

172

hardly be tribal leaders otherwise. His father still lives at Biu and is the only cultivator of grapes for miles and miles around. Mai Sule hopes to lead his father to Christ.

How did a Muslim prince become a Christian minister? That is a story in itself. Along about 1932, when Mai Sule was a lad of twelve, he noticed strange spots on his skin. When the rest of his skin perspired, these spots stayed dry. He heard some people of his tribe whispering about him one day.

"Those spots on Mai Sule — they look like leprosy spots. Could a prince have leprosy? Perhaps we should take him to that new American doctor at Virgwi-Garkida."

Leprosy? American doctor? Mai Sule wanted to hide. Everyone knew that it was the custom of those white men to add to their meat diet by eating unlucky natives. What a spot for a twelve-year-old to be in! But since native medicines could never help leprosy the chief told his personal bodyguard to escort the young prince to Virgwi.

But the first visit to Virgwi was anything but encouraging. As it happened, they found Doctor Howard Bosler preparing for an operation. Mai Sule saw how carefully the body of the patient was cleansed. He saw the rows of clean dishes and instruments and the array of knives — just as if they were getting ready to carve up a market cow. He saw how, as the doctor cut away small bits of flesh during the operation, they were dropped into one of the pans. Obviously, it was a preparation for cooking. The reports were true: these white men did indeed eat human flesh — if not the whole body, then at least selected parts.

Mai Sule left as quickly as possible. And, strangely enough, the guards were more than willing to follow close behind him. Native medicine would have to do. The witch doctor would have to throw the demons of leprosy out. He was a fright to look at, but at least he had a different kind of appetite.

Of course the witch doctor's treatment was a failure. As another year passed, his friends noticed that Mai Sule's hands were becoming clawlike; the finger joints were contracting and the leprosy was gaining. They would have to try the American doctor again.

And like a miracle — although a slow miracle which involved hundreds of injections of chaulmoogra oil and took many years in the process — the leprosy was checked. The day finally came when there were no more signs of its activity. But a bigger miracle was taking place at the same time, that of education and of conversion to Christ.

Out of those miracles — and out of the background of Mai Sule's having been born to leadership — have come years of service for the church. He served as a dispenser, injector, and hospital attendant. He served as a teacher, himself with only five years of elementary school and a year of instruction in how to teach. He served as a local church leader. He attended the Bible school. He attended the pastor's class under the teaching of Ira Petre. He was licensed to the ministry, then ordained, and then, on that memorable June 22, 1958, he was installed as the first Nigerian elder in the Church of the Brethren.

If you talk with Mai Sule today, he will begin by giving generous praise to the Brethren whom God has called to this country. He will say, again and again: "My gratitude is beyond telling, for we who had leprosy were twice saved by God — once saved from our leprosy and once from our sin. There can't be any greater love than this."

He will point with pride to his good wife, Gana, who serves beside him in the church, leading the women and teaching them, and shouldering the larger share of rearing their family. He will point to their family of seven.

"There are my three boys: Ali, who was named to show his royal blood; Gamaliel, named for the teacher of the Apostle Paul; Bosler, named after that doctor who scared me so badly! There are my four girls: Rifkatu (Rebecca); Arziki; Ladi (Sunday); Shisler, named after Miss Sara Shisler, who taught me a great deal about the Bible. God has given us a good family."

He will tell you about his hopes and his problems.

"I wish I had some kind of good transportation. A bicycle is all right, but I would like to be able to go to visit local churches and village groups in many places and tell them about Jesus. What I most want next is a chance to learn a great deal of English [he is talking in Bura, you see]. There are good books in English which would help me to be a better shepherd for my people.

"I wish that we could win more Muslims for Christ. I wish that we could have more workers. There are many people who want to know, and few to teach them. The fields are white. 'Pray that the lord of the harvest may send more workers.' I wish our local churches would do better at supporting the outvillage work. I wish that we might have a church-wide program of Bible teaching and leadership training."

But he not only wishes; he also prays. And he works to make his wishes be answered and his prayers come true. A man of deep concern, pastor of the flock, beloved by his people, writer and enthusiastic leader of songs, dramatic dispenser of Christian truths — this is Elder Mai Sule. Once an African prince, he has more recently been called of God to be a prince of the church.

— Ishaku Boroma Bdliya

175

An Apostle of Brotherly Love

MICHAEL ROBERT ZIGLER (1891 –)

Jesus loved everyone. The disciples who walked with Him in Galilee and Judea learned from Him that they should love everyone. The early church accepted His way of love and forgiveness and His peaceful method of treating enemies. For several hundred years in that early time Christians would have no part in war or any other kind of violence.

But there came a time in the fourth century A.D. when the church gave up its pacifist position. "That was a disaster," wrote a Dutch scholar. "The worst of it is . . . what was evil was called good."

Today there are in the world many Christians who do not claim to be pacifists. They think that if and when a war comes they should do their part in it. In the First World War there were only a few hundred ministers in the United States who were courageous enough to speak against war. In the Second World War there were many more, both ministers and laymen, who claimed conscientious objection to war, who believed that it is always wrong to kill men.

Michael Robert Zigler is one who has stood for the pacifist position like a shining light in the Church of the Brethren. He firmly believes that it is wrong for men to kill each other. He believes that Christians should unite on this teaching of Jesus, "Love your enemies and pray for those who persecute you." He has spent much of his life preaching, counseling, teaching, and searching for that which will stir Christians to desire to make Jesus' teachings their rule for living.

M. R. (Bob) Zigler grew up in Virginia. His grandparents had been near neighbors of John Kline, a martyr to the cause of peace during the Civil War. Bob never forgot the story of John Kline. He admired the courage of men like him and Peter Wrightsman. Sometimes he wondered: "Why didn't more Brethren have the courage to stand in front of government officials and declare that war is wrong? Would I have such courage?"

While Bob was still a young man our country was at war with Germany. He had graduated from Bridgewater College and was in the School of Religion at Vanderbilt University about the time the war started. The YMCA provided the opening for him to do something that was not fighting, something that offered opportunity to witness to Jesus' gospel of love and peace. He was sent to Parris Island, South Carolina, to direct recreation for the Marines who used the facilities of the YMCA.

He stayed in this work for more than two years. He would talk with Marines who had no heart for what they were doing. They did not think either that war was right. "Why does one get sent to prison if he kills a man in his home town, while here we are trained to kill men in the name of our government?" a Marine asked him. Bob also talked to commanding officers. And sometimes they got on the subject of the right and the wrong of war. Little did he think then that some twenty years later he would be calling on generals and government officials in Washington to uphold the rights of young men whose consciences would not allow them to take military training.

In 1919 M. R. Zigler was called by the Church of the

Brethren to go to the church headquarters in Elgin, Illinois, to serve the entire Brotherhood. He was to give help to the smaller churches, some of whom had no pastors. These churches needed to have someone talk with them and give them courage and strength. So he became the home mission secretary. In that work he had a rich experience for ten years. Many people in the churches across our land learned to know, love, and trust him. They were encouraged by his wise counsel and their faith was strengthened. Later he was made the executive secretary of the ministerial board of the church, and then the executive secretary of Christian education. While continuing to live in Elgin, he was often in other places, for he was finding ever-wider areas in which to share his Christian faith.

In the 1930's the leaders of the church were much troubled about the events taking place in the world. But they were even more concerned about the lack of conviction, courage, and faith among Christian people. Bob Zigler came back from Europe in 1937 saying that a war was coming. He was disturbed about the young men who might be called to give military service. He urged that the leaders of the Church of the Brethren should unite with leaders of the other peace churches (the Quakers and the Mennonites) to talk with our government about providing for young men whose consciences would not allow them to engage in military service. It was pointed out that the Constitution of the United States provides for freedom of a man's conscience. Brother Zigler became one of the chief spokesmen before government officials on this matter.

As a result of these efforts, Congress agreed to another type of service for those who could not take military training because of their consciences. A little later, civilian public service camps were set up at various places across the country. Young men who were conscientious objectors to war lived in these camps, cleared forests, put up buildings, checked forest fires, and did other useful work. Others worked in state mental hospitals and on farms.

At about the same time, Brother Zigler became the executive secretary of the Committee for Conscientious Objectors, the executive secretary of the Brethren Service Committee, and the chairman of the National Service Board for Religious Objectors. Eventually he was able to

take to the World Council of Churches his hope that the various governments would provide for their conscientious objectors. As time went on he became more and more hopeful. His dream was coming true. More and more people were sharing in his concern.

His ambition has been to encourage the Church of the Brethren to be a leading peacemaking church in the world, using our lives and means to that end. "The world needs the message which the church has," he says, "and

179

we have the man power and the resources. Many would join with us in this effort if we were sincere and aggressive and really would bear the cross to achieve the goal."

When M. R. wrote these words he knew what suffering means. This was in the late summer of 1958 after the tragedy of the automobile accident in Sweden and the K.L.M. plane explosion over the Atlantic. Three persons, one of whom was Mrs. Zigler, had lost their lives in the car collision. And twenty Brethren had gone down on the plane.

M. R. lay in a hospital in Sweden for long weeks. He suffered from a broken body and the grief of losing his companion and the friends to whom he said good-by before they got on the plane to return to America. His work in Europe had ended, he thought. There was no home to return to in America. He was retired from his work with the Brethren Service Commission.

But his work was not done. Though his body was weak and immovable he was a stalwart witness to the purpose to which he had dedicated his life. The doctor who took care of him had lost his Christian faith during the war when he was cruelly mistreated by soldiers of a so-called Christian nation. M. R. was able to help the doctor find his faith again. The two men became close friends, sharing a deep interest in the spread of Christian brotherhood and love.

Brother Zigler was restored. He was able to get on a ship and come back to the United States. After he had been here for a while he started on a tour of the churches to give his message. If you heard him you know what his message was. He stirred the hearts of older and younger to listen again for the messages that came from the early Christian movement.

"On earth peace among men" were the words that

had announced the coming of Jesus into the world.

"Seek first his kingdom and his righteousness" were the words Jesus proclaimed at the height of his ministry.

"Go therefore and make disciples" were the final words to His followers before He went away.

These three messages, M. R. Zigler said, lingered in his mind when he lay helpless in the hospital. They were his texts as he went about among the churches, urging that Christian people seek, with all the means possible, to establish brotherhood, goodwill, and peace; to proclaim once more that the way of love and forgiveness is more important than any other way for men to live together. His deep concern and his enthusiasm for peaceful ways of dealing with persons and nations will not be lost if we follow his leading.

— Edith Barnes

From Log Cabin to the Presidency

C. ERNEST DAVIS (1893 —)

Though the distance from a log cabin to the presidency of a Brethren college may not be as great as that covered by Abraham Lincoln in his career, yet the fact that C. Ernest Davis didn't get started until some eighty-four years after Lincoln (when there weren't nearly so many log cabins around in which one could be born) does put his accomplishment into the same class with that of Honest Abe.

It is hardly believable that Ernest Davis, whom many space-age youngsters know personally — you may have heard him speak at an Annual Conference, for he has attended every one of them since 1924 and has very often appeared on the platform; you may have heard him at a regional or district conference; or it may be that he has been a guest speaker in your local church, for he has probably visited in as many congregations as has anybody else in our Brotherhood — who recently flew around the world, and who is as "up" on modern developments as anyone, actually was born in a log cabin in the hills of Tennessee, "came west" to the California frontier ahead of the railroad, and was, in fact, a part of the homesteader and family-farm movement that pushed the cattle barons off the ranges.

The story of his life falls into a teeter-totter pattern, that is, two ends balanced against each other across a center pivot. The center of his life, quite clearly, has been *the church* — the Church of the Brethren in particular. The first end of the teeter board (the "down" end that carried the weight during his early years) was *how the church helped mold the man;* the second end, which has carried the weight since his adulthood, has been *how the man helped mold the church.*

Obviously, times have changed so much since Ernest Davis was a boy that there is perhaps but little which modern young people can copy directly from his experience, but this pattern is one that will hold good in any age, under any conditions. It is a pattern guaranteed to produce both good men and a good church. If one will let his life be molded and shaped by the church and then give that life to the service of the church, there can be no question that the individual will have a happy, productive life and that the church will have the sort of leadership which will make it strong and effective.

Ernest Davis was practically born into the Church of the Brethren, we might say. His grandfather, who made his living as a clerk on the steamboats that then sailed the Ohio River, served the church as an unsalaried (or free) minister. Ernest's father was a farmer-preacher, and his Uncle John Davis was a deacon. His mother died when he was but six weeks old, and he was taken out of his log-cabin home to another part of Tennessee where his Uncle John and Aunt Martha raised him and became, in effect, his parents. The church in which Ernest grew up — the New Hope congregation at McKenzie, Tennessee — was so small, so scattered, and so poor that it did not have a church building but held services in the schoolhouse or in private homes. At the age of eight, Ernest gave his life to Christ.

And strange as it may seem, the move that the Davises

made when Ernest was fourteen, the change from being Tennessee farmers to becoming settlers on the far-off California frontier, was also done at the encouragement of the church. At this time (1907) the Brethren were promoting a program known as "church extension through colonization"; by means of its magazines and papers, speakers and traveling "agents," the church persuaded Eastern Brethren to settle the new farmlands of the West by migrating in groups, so that they could establish communities which would support strong, growing churches and thus spread the gospel into new territory.

The colony to which the Davises came was Butte Valley, in the high, timbered plateau country along the northern border of California. The settlement had been in existence less than a year when the Davises arrived. And what proved to be very important for Ernest's life was the fact that a Brethren family from Kansas had settled in the community just a month before. One of the girls in this Heisel family — Grace by name — later became Ernest's wife and the mother of their five children.

When the Davises arrived in Butte Valley, the means of transportation were still stagecoach and freighter-wagons (the Union Pacific railroad came through a few years later). The Brethren had organized a congregation and were in the process of building a meetinghouse but were for the present holding services in a tent (like the ancient Israelites with their tabernacle). There was as yet no public school in the area; so the Brethren hired one of the "sisters" of the congregation to teach the children. Ernest had already had one year of "high school" (eighth grade) in Tennessee, but since he wanted to continue his schooling he had no choice but to take eighth-grade material again at Butte Valley, because that was as high as the private teacher could go. The next year, when a public school was established in Butte Valley, Ernest went through the eighth grade a third time in order to get a certificate of graduation.

However, Ernest had done a thorough enough job at the eighth-grade level that he was able to enter high school as a sophomore. But going to high school meant a six-hundred-mile train ride to the Brethren school in southern California, Lordsburg Academy (the high-school branch of what was later renamed La Verne College). Between this time (1910) and 1923, he spent six years at La Verne completing his high-school and college work. The church, through its educational program, was certainly doing a job of "life-molding" on this young man.

Money wasn't as easy to come by in those days as it is now, and Ernest had to make his own way without help from home — although even in this the church gave a helping hand. One of the Brethren whom Ernest met at a Northern California district meeting helped the young student locate a part-time job at La Verne. Ernest also depended on summer work at home in the woods and the sawmill ($2.75 for a ten-hour day); and the summer he was laid up as the result of a logging accident one of the Butte Valley Brethren loaned him money so that he could go back to school.

It was during these La Verne days that the teeter began to tip toward the second end of the board: Ernest was beginning to have some molding influence upon the church. During his first summer home from the academy he was elected to the ministry; and less than seven years later he was advanced to the eldership. In the course of the six-year period between his academy (high school) and his college work at La Verne he got married, taught school, and held his first pastorate. He served the church in Chico, California, for fifty dollars per month and an eight-dollar rent allowance. While Ernest was growing up, the church was changing from the free ministry to the salaried ministry — though, goodness knows, it is difficult to say in which class fifty-eight dollars per month belongs! When he went back to college, he was molding as well as being molded, for he earned his way by teaching in the academy, supervising the boys' dormitory, supplying a pulpit, and doing field work for the college.

Since his college days (the period which represents the greater part of his life, though we can discuss it only briefly here), Ernest Davis has given himself completely as a leader and molder of the life of the church. He has been a pastor and a district fieldman in the areas of temperance and religious education. He has been president of two of our colleges (Mt. Morris and his alma mater, La Verne) and a teacher at a third (McPherson). He has served on various general boards of the Brotherhood continuously from 1927 until 1948; and from 1948 to 1958 he was the head of the Christian education program for the entire Brotherhood. He has held almost every office that our Annual Conference organization has to offer. And now, since his retirement, he is still spending his time visiting the churches, providing them leadership and help.

Surely, the almost-fifty years of devoted service given by Brother Davis have played a considerable part in molding our church into its present form. And what is it that made possible this career which has been so rewarding both to him and to the whole Church of the Brethren? Of course, much of the credit must go to C. Ernest Davis as a person; but beyond this lies the secret that the church molded him before he molded it.

— *Vernard M. Eller*

186

A Life Lived for Peace

DAN WEST (1893 –)

The red-orange light of the campfire threw shadows on the faces of the campers under the trees. It outlined the speaker standing near the center of the circle. Suddenly the fire flashed, tracing sharply in light and shade the profile of the man.

He spoke in a casual manner, his shirt open loosely at the throat, his sleeves folded back in neat carelessness below the elbow. Bending easily toward the campers as he spoke, he was like a giant willow at the lake shore leaning toward the wellsprings of its life. Even as he spoke to the youth around the campfire he was learning from them. That speaker, Dan West, has taken the vigor of his youthful audiences to put force into ideas that will grow for many years to come.

Under the trees the campfire died; but other fires of a different kind were built on the dead embers. Time has moved over the embers of this campfire and campfires like it scattered over a vast area from the Blue Ridge Mountains across the prairies to the shores washed by the Pacific. Years have passed over the lives of hundreds of Brethren youth and their leaders. And the man who spoke under the trees that night has met these years with a giant's stature, tall and willowy still.

Forty years later, in a discussion room at the Brethren Service Center at New Windsor, Maryland, he sits within a circle of youth. This time he is listening and speaking to young Brethren preparing for an adventure — an adventure of Christian love and service.

Dan's grey-blue eyes, set below eyebrows that are now white, look at the young with the same spirit of adventure which lighted his own youthful eyes years ago. Alone, he had left his childhood home in southern Ohio to find out whether the ideas preached in the plain brick Brethren meetinghouse a mile and a half away would work in places a hundred miles away, then a thousand miles away, and finally halfway around the world. He believed that they would. This adventure was his and his alone at first. He had to make it while young and he had to make it on his own. He had a burning curiosity to find out whether the only way of life he had ever known was important enough to hold his respect and his loyalty for a lifetime.

Now he knows that his curiosity has been satisfied. His experiences have given him some of the answers. His earliest adventure and many others in later years have given him a new confidence in the teachings of his home and his church. Yet, as he talks with the youth of the church, he never pushes his own discoveries upon them.

The young people wait for his answers, but Dan will not give answers. He believes that young people have a storehouse of natural courage and faith. He believes that they need nothing so much as leaders who assure them that the answers can be discovered in their own adventures. He further believes that adults have no right to deny youth the adventure of discovering what their own place in life is. Much of this is an individual adventure which he will not spoil by giving out secondhand definitions. He believes that young people need encouragement, a square look at the ground rules, and a few basic directions. From these they will make their own discoveries. Dan has given a deep, silent faith to Brethren youth.

It was while Dan was in Spain as a relief worker that he saw what could be done by Christians who cared for those in need. He came back to the States with a simple plea, "The people of Spain are hungry." The message struck home to the tender hearts of well-fed Brethren. They responded with the heifer project, in which heifers could be shipped to needy families abroad. Now children could have milk and farmers could have something with which to start life again. Practical religion was in Dan's mind when he started talking about sending heifers to people starved by war. Here was religion so practical, so down to earth, that people could milk it! Here was a way of saying that since the Brethren cannot destroy in war they must be constructive Christians.

This direct, hand-to-hand giving of the Christian was a common practice in the Landon West home, into which Dan was born. Dan's parents were not young when he was born, and by the time he was in his growing years his parents' hands had known half a lifetime of helping those in need. They were hands experienced at the business of being their brother's keeper. While Landon West preached this ideal in various places, his wife and family tried to live his words at home. The combination of word and hand runs like a thread through Dan's life. Even today, his work with people and ideas is combined with manual work on his farm near Goshen, Indiana, where he has lived for over twenty years with his wife, Lucy, and their five children.

College classes, physical work, and life in big cities only strengthened the ideas which he had heard preached on Sunday and which he had seen in action among the Brethren on weekdays. At Columbia University in New

York City, far distant from Preble County, Ohio, it suddenly flashed upon his mind one day that one of his professors was saying some of the same things that his mother had taught him, and almost in the same language. The combined strength of two persons unknown to each other gave power to the ideas which they shared. This has been Dan's own teaching method with young people; he believes that shared ideas are stronger ideas.

Slowly the conviction grew in Dan's young mind that his Brethren forefathers had a great deal to offer. To save the best part of what the Brethren have to offer, and to combine it with the best from other sources, has been his hope. It has kept him restless, for he knows that careless people sometimes throw out riches if they do not know their worth. He has dedicated himself to conserving what is good.

In Dan's early manhood he took a place of leadership in summer church camps, which were then still new among the Brethren. For many years in the 1920's he combined his three major interests in camp work: people, ideas, and out of doors. During these years he linked his camp work in summer with a career as a teacher of biology, then as the principal, at the Trotwood high school, in Ohio. In 1930 the church called him to full-time work as the national youth director with his office at Elgin, Illinois.

His love for people made him sensitive to the injustices settling down upon Europe like heavy clouds about to break out in war. His love for peace and the peace position of the church moved him into action. In 1936 he began his long, hard struggle to help the Brethren to see that war was contrary to the will of God.

A trip to Europe some eight years before, and his guilt feelings over his military service in the First World

War, had sparked Dan's personal peace convictions into an open witness against war. Yet to be against war did not seem to be enough for a peace church. Taking seriously the ideas of Matthew 18, Dan began to learn all he could about how to treat people so that they would have no reason to go to war. To work for the prevention of war was a forward step for the Brethren in the mid-thirties. Before this, the church had scarcely touched the problem of war except to say that it was wrong.

As the church began to have a healthy respect for its own peace testimony, it began to ask the government to respect it also. This new self-respect about the peace position of the church helped to prepare the way for the civilian public service camps which the church and the government established during World War II.

The Brethren and the world at large have begun to learn in a new way the importance of working for peace. On the heels of the last war, a program to promote peace began. Tons and tons of clothing and food were shipped abroad through Brethren Service, later expanded into Church World Service. Heifers, bulls, chickens, bees, and goats were sent abroad to needy families. International work camps were established to promote understanding among youth of different nations. Brethren Volunteer Service, which trains young people for constructive service to the church, was a dream of Dan's a decade before it actually began. He has worked to make Brethren ideals and ideas loved and lovable, especially to the young. He believes that our best ideas are workable and that the world needs them. He has begun programs and projects to prove that they will work.

The distant horizons are bright in his eyes — the eyes of a natural pioneer. He has kept the straightness of the pine trees in his stature. But his roots are deep in his native soil. That soil is the Brethren heritage with the best it has to offer. Where the Brethren heritage has been barren and almost fruitless, Dan has not destroyed it or neglected it. He has never sold it short. He has sought to enrich it and to help it fulfill its purpose. And while he lifts his head with dignity in great towering ideas, he spends most of his time carefully tending this soil. When the seedbed is ready, he bends tenderly over each fragile new growth. Many of the fruits which will blossom from the soil in future years will come from ideas which Dan has planted.

You can watch him yet, waiting for the seed to take root, never giving up the hope that it will yield — if not for him, then for many others even for generations to come. It is the eternal hope of the cultivator of the soil. It is the demand of the age in which we live that the soil must be made ready if peace is to flourish. This is the conviction and the steady labor of Dan West, a man dedicated to cultivating the soil for peace.

— Inez Goughnour Long